The Azar-Hagen Grammar Series

TEST BANK for

BASIC
English
Grammar

FOURTH EDITION

Kelly Roberts Weibel

Basic English Grammar, Fourth Edition
Test Bank

Azar Associates: Shelley Hartle, Editor, and Sue Van Etten, Manager

Pearson Education, 10 Bank Street, White Plains, NY 10606

Staff credits: The people who made up the *Basic English Grammar,
Fourth Edition, Test Bank* team, representing editorial, production,
design, and manufacturing, are, Nancy Flaggman, Amy McCormick,
Robert Ruvo, Ruth Voetmann, and Marian Wassner.

Text composition: S4Carlisle Publishing Services

Printed in the United States of America

ISBN 10: 0-13-343837-6
ISBN 13: 978-0-13-343837-6

1 2 3 4 5 6 7 8 9 10—V001—19 18 17 16 15 14

CONTENTS

This test bank accompanies *Basic English Grammar, Fourth Edition*. Instructors can choose from over 200 quizzes and thirty-two tests to use for assessment. Teachers familiar with the fourth edition will find a great deal of material has been updated for this fourth edition.

QUIZZES

Each chapter contains a series of quizzes keyed to individual charts in the student book, followed by two chapter tests. The quizzes are intended as quick checks of student understanding for both teacher and student. Mastery of a quiz is a strong indicator that students are ready to progress to the next section.

CHAPTER TESTS

The tests at the end of each chapter are comprehensive, covering as many points from the chapter as possible. The formats of the questions in the chapter tests follow those used in the previous quizzes. The two chapter tests are identical in format so that one may be used as a practice test if desired.

EXAMS

Two midterm exams covering chapters one through seven and two comprehensive final exams are included in this test bank. They can be used in conjunction with the other quizzes and tests, or used separately.

FORMAT

Because students bring a variety of learning styles to the classroom, there is a wide selection of test formats, including sentence completion, sentence connection, multiple choice, and error analysis, as well as more open completion. To maximize the use of the answer key, open-ended writing practice has been kept to a minimum. Teachers wishing to incorporate more writing into the tests are encouraged to add their own material at the end of the chapter tests.

ANSWER KEY

An answer key for all quizzes, tests, and exams can be found in the back of the text.

DUPLICATION

The material has been formatted so teachers can easily make copies for their students. Permission is granted to duplicate as many copies as needed for classroom use only.

Acknowledgements

This work wouldn't have been possible without the love and support of my family, who keep me in touch with natural-sounding English and give me valuable feedback. Thanks, guys! I also want to thank my colleagues at Edmonds Community College for their encouragement. Special thanks, once again, to Ruth Voetmann and Stacy Hagen, for making this project such a pleasure to work on.

CHAPTER 1 Using *Be*

QUIZ 1 **Singular Pronouns** (Chart 1-1)

Directions: Write the correct pronoun. Use **he, she,** or **it.**

Example: my father _____*he*_____

1. Miss Kennedy _____   6. George _____

2. a cat _____   7. Japanese _____

3. Mr. Rolland _____   8. Mrs. Yang _____

4. Sandra _____   9. my brother _____

5. Australia _____   10. the bus _____

QUIZ 2 **Singular Pronouns + *Be*** (Chart 1-1)

Directions: Complete the sentences with **am, is,** or **are.** Change nouns to pronouns.

Example: (*Cathleen*) _____*She is*_____ nice.

1. (*Mr. Jones*) _____ friendly.

2. You _____ hungry.

3. (*Matt*) _____ sleepy.

4. (*my dinner*) _____ delicious.

5. I _____ tired.

6. (*the bus*) _____ late.

7. (*Alexandra*) _____ very smart.

8. You _____ funny.

9. I _____ serious.

10. (*the mouse*) _____ small.

Plural Pronouns + *Be* (Chart 1-2)

A. ***Directions:*** Choose the correct pronoun. The first one is an example.

1. my father and my mother   we   you   (they)
2. you and Arturo   we   you   they
3. my sister and I   we   you   they
4. Ali and you   we   you   they
5. Max and Martina   we   you   they
6. Ms. Zahra and I   we   you   they

B. ***Directions:*** Complete the sentences. Use ***we, you,*** or ***they.*** The first one is an example.

1. Maria and you are here. _____*You*_____ are hungry.

2. David and I are in a hurry. _____ are late.

3. Mr. and Mrs. Al-Sultan are friendly. _____ are nice.

4. Marcos and Charles are here. _____ are tired.

5. My brother and I are hot. _____ are sick.

6. You and Alicia are ready. _____ are happy.

Pronouns + *Be* (Charts 1-1 and 1-2)

Directions: Complete the sentences. Use ***am, is,*** or ***are.***

Example: Mr. Herrera works at the bookstore. He _____*is*_____ kind.

Situation: *Meet Miguel's Family*

1. My name is Miguel. I _____ Mexican.

2. I have one brother and one sister. They _____ smart.

3. Roberto is my brother. He _____ 20 years old.

4. My brother and I live at home. We _____ happy.

5. My sister lives in an apartment. She _____ homesick.

6. My parents work hard. They _____ tired.

7. My grandmother cooks dinner for us. She _____ kind.

8. My uncle lives with us. He _____ funny.

9. I have a dog. It _____ cute.

10. I like you. You _____ friendly.

Directions: Write *a* or *an*. The first one is an example.

1. __*a*__ country

2. _____ animal

3. _____ bird

4. _____ island

5. _____ friend

6. _____ day

7. _____ hotel

8. _____ teacher

9. _____ office

10. _____ city

11. _____ avenue

Directions: Complete the sentences. Use *a* or *an* and the words in the box. Use each word only once. The first one is an example.

animal	city	country	island	sport	✓vegetable
book	color	girl	language	street	

1. An onion is __*a vegetable*__ .

2. Japanese is _____ .

3. France is _____ .

4. A dictionary is _____ .

5. Rome is _____ .

6. Basketball is _____ .

7. A dog is _____ .

8. Broadway is _____ .

9. Maria is _____ .

10. Red is _____ .

11. Bali is _____ .

Directions: Change the singular sentences to plural sentences.

Examples: A Volkswagen is a car. _Volkswagens are cars._

Asia is a continent.
South America is a continent. _Asia and South America are continents._

1. A cat is an animal. _____

2. A rose is a flower. _____

3. A hotel is a building. _____

4. A computer is a machine. _____

5. A dictionary is a book. _____

6. London is a city.
    Chicago is a city. _____

7. French is a language.
    Arabic is a language. _____

8. Tennis is a sport.
    Baseball is a sport. _____

9. Dyanne is a teacher.
    Fatima is a teacher. _____

10. Summer is a season.
    Winter is a season. _____

Nouns and Pronouns + Be (Charts 1-1 → 1-4)

Directions: Make complete sentences. Use *am, is,* or *are*.

Examples: Seattle \ a city. _____Seattle is a city._____

I \ thirsty. _____I am thirsty._____

1. You (one person) \ beautiful _____.

2. Spring \ a season _____.

3. A rose \ a flower _____.

4. We \ hungry _____.

5. A bird \ an animal _____.

6. They \ funny _____.

7. I \ a singer _____.

8. Egypt and Italy \ countries _____.

9. You (two persons) \ students _____.

10. Carrots \ vegetables _____.

Contractions with *Be* (Chart 1-5)

Directions: Complete the sentences with pronouns. Use contractions.

Example: **Mariko** is from Japan. _____She's_____ my classmate.

1. **I** go to school. _____ a student.

2. I have one **brother**. _____ eighteen years old.

3. I have one **sister**. _____ married.

4. **Ali and I** are friends. _____ in the same class.

5. I have two **books**. _____ on the table.

6. I like **Mrs. Pieters**. _____ my teacher.

7. **Paulo** is in my class. _____ from Brazil.

8. I know **Jin and Young**. _____ very friendly.

9. Hannes is from **Vienna**. _____ a big city.

10. I like **you**. _____ very funny.

Directions: Complete the sentences. Use ***is, are, isn't,*** or ***aren't***. Use the given information.

Examples: California = state

California _____*is*_____ a state. It _____*isn't*_____ a city.

Canada and China = countries

Canada and China _____*aren't*_____ continents. They _____*are*_____ countries.

1. Tokyo = city

   Tokyo _____ a city. It _____ a country.

2. you = student

   You _____ a student. You _____ a plumber.

3. Ms. Gockley = teacher

   Ms. Gockley _____ a bus driver. She _____ a teacher.

4. Jim and Yasuko = gardeners

   Jim and Yasuko _____ gardeners. They _____ astronauts.

5. Mato and I = police officers

   Mato and I _____ doctors. We _____ police officers.

Directions: Write the contractions for each given sentence.

Example: It is not a country.

   It _____*'s not*_____ a country. OR It _____*isn't*_____ a country.

1. They are not doctors.

   They _____ doctors. OR They _____ doctors.

2. He is not a nurse.

   He _____ a nurse. OR He _____ a nurse.

3. She is not a construction worker.

   She _____ a construction worker. OR She _____ a construction worker.

4. We are not gardeners.

   We _____ gardeners. OR We _____ gardeners.

5. You are not teachers.

   You _____ teachers. OR You _____ teachers.

6. I am not an auto mechanic.

   I _____ an auto mechanic.

Directions: Write the adjective with the opposite meaning. Use the words in the box.
The first one is an example.

beautiful	dangerous	happy	sick	tall	warm
cheap	dirty	poor	✓small	uncrowded	
cold	dry	quiet	sour	unfriendly	

1. big _____ *small* _____

2. clean _____

3. friendly _____

4. safe _____

5. ugly _____

6. noisy _____

7. crowded _____

8. hot _____

9. cool _____

10. expensive _____

11. wet _____

12. sad _____

13. sweet _____

14. rich _____

15. short _____

16. well _____

Directions: Underline the adjective in the first sentence. Complete the second sentence with ***be*** + an adjective with an opposite meaning. Use each adjective from the box only once. The first one is an example.

> √ beautiful   cold   old   sad   slow   tall
> clean   dry   poor   safe   sour

1. Roses aren't <u>ugly</u>. They ___*'re beautiful.*___

2. Lemons aren't sweet. They _____.

3. My apartment isn't dirty. It _____.

4. Mrs. Andreason isn't rich. She _____.

5. Turtles aren't fast. They _____.

6. Jonathan isn't hot. He _____.

7. Deserts aren't wet. They _____.

8. My car isn't new. It _____.

9. Anna isn't happy. She _____.

10. Henri isn't short. He _____.

11. This city isn't dangerous. It _____.

Directions: Write two sentences. Use ***be*** and the given words. Make the first sentence negative. Use a pronoun in the second sentence.

Example: airplanes . . . slow / fast

      Airplanes aren't slow.   *They're fast.*

1. lemons . . . red / yellow

   _____   _____

2. English . . . easy / difficult

   _____   _____

3. balls . . . square / round

   _____   _____

4. a pen . . . heavy / light

   _____   _____

5. a mouse . . . big / little

   _____   _____

Directions: Complete each sentence with the correct preposition in the box. You can use a preposition more than once. The first one is an example.

✓ above	between	next to	under
behind	in	on	

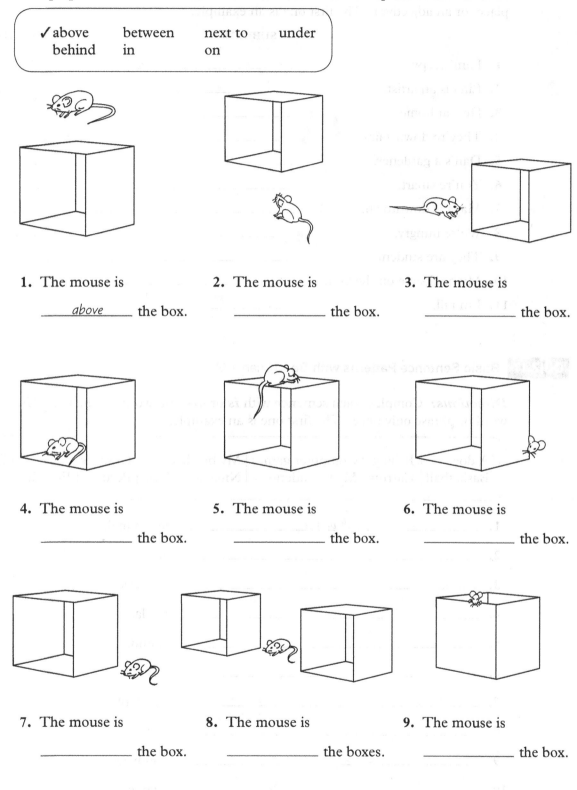

1. The mouse is

_____*above*_____ the box.

2. The mouse is

_____ the box.

3. The mouse is

_____ the box.

4. The mouse is

_____ the box.

5. The mouse is

_____ the box.

6. The mouse is

_____ the box.

7. The mouse is

_____ the box.

8. The mouse is

_____ the boxes.

9. The mouse is

_____ the box.

Basic Sentence Patterns with *Be* (Chart 1-9)

Directions: Write the subject of each sentence. Write the form of *be* (*am, is,* or *are*) used in each sentence. Then write the grammar structure that follows *be* (a noun, a place, or an adjective). The first one is an example.

	SUBJECT	+	*BE*	+	COMPLETION
1. I am sleepy.	*I*		*am*		*adjective*
2. Lina is an artist.					
3. He's at home.					
4. They're downstairs.					
5. Dan's a gardener.					
6. You're smart.					
7. Maya is downtown.					
8. We're hungry.					
9. They are students.					
10. My books are on the table.					
11. I'm tall.					

QUIZ 17 **Basic Sentence Patterns with *Be*** (Chart 1-9)

Directions: Complete each sentence with *is* or *are* and words in the box. Use each word or phrase only once. The first one is an example.

✓A dog	Beijing	Computer games	My brother	Oranges	Spanish
Basketball	Carrots	Many students	Nina and Maria	Peru and Ecuador	

1. _____ *A dog is* _____ an animal.

2. _____ sisters.

3. _____ homesick.

4. _____ in class.

5. _____ round.

6. _____ a sport.

7. _____ vegetables.

8. _____ a city.

9. _____ countries.

10. _____ a language.

11. _____ fun.

CHAPTER 1–TEST 1

Part A   *Directions:* Change the singular sentences to plural sentences.

1. An onion is a vegetable.   _____

2. A bird is an animal.   _____

3. A lemon is yellow.   _____

4. Jakarta is a city.
   Seoul is a city.   _____

5. Tennis is a sport.
   Soccer is a sport.   _____

Part B   *Directions:* Complete the sentences with pronouns + *be*. Use contractions.

1. I have **a dictionary**. _____ on the table.

2. **My sister** is thirty-five years old. _____ an astronaut.

3. **Jorge and Masako** are students. _____ in my class.

4. I have **one brother**. _____ nineteen years old.

5. **I** like school. _____ happy.

Part C   *Directions:* Complete the sentences with the negative form of *be*.

1. London _____ a country.

2. Cats and dogs _____ birds.

3. I _____ nervous.

4. Mrs. Bilova _____ at home now.

5. You _____ here.

Part D   *Directions:* Make sentences with *is, isn't, are,* and *aren't.*

1. Cars \ cheap . . . They \ expensive

   _____

2. A rose \ ugly . . . It \ beautiful

   _____

3. Lemons \ sweet . . . They \ sour

   _____

4. Grammar \ difficult . . . It \ easy

   _____

5. Jonas \ an adult . . . He \ a child

   _____

Directions: Complete the sentences. Choose from the words in the box.

above	between	next to	under
behind	in	on	

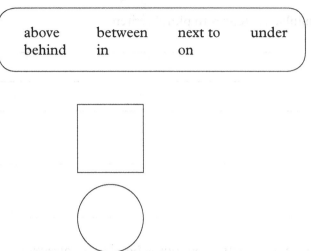

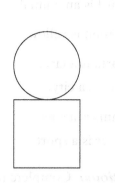

1. The circle is _____ the square.

2. The circle is _____ the square.

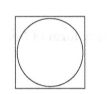

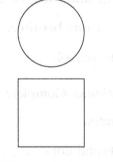

3. The circle is _____ the square.

4. The circle is _____ the square.

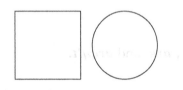

5. The circle is _____ the square.

CHAPTER 1–TEST 2

Part A *Directions:* Change the singular sentences to plural sentences.

1. A dictionary is a book. _____

2. A ball is round. _____

3. An airplane is fast. _____

4. Chinese is a language.
   Japanese is a language. _____

5. Cuba is a country.
   Turkey is a country. _____

Part B *Directions:* Complete the sentences with pronouns + *be*. Use contractions.

1. I like **grammar**. _____ interesting.

2. **My brother and I** go to school. _____ students.

3. My parents live in **an apartment**. _____ on First Street.

4. I know **Mr. Smith**. _____ very friendly.

5. I have **two books and a pen**. _____ on my desk.

Part C *Directions:* Complete the sentences with the negative form of *be*.

1. Africa _____ a city.

2. My clothes _____ dirty.

3. We _____ outside now.

4. He _____ from Cuba.

5. I _____ at work today.

Part D *Directions:* Make sentences with *is, isn't, are,* and *aren't.*

1. A box \ round . . . It \ square

   _____

2. The sun \ hot . . . It \ cold

   _____

3. Bananas \ blue . . . They \ yellow

   _____

4. Rain forests \ wet . . . They \ dry

   _____

5. A coin \ large . . . It \ small

   _____

above	between	next to	under
behind	in	on	

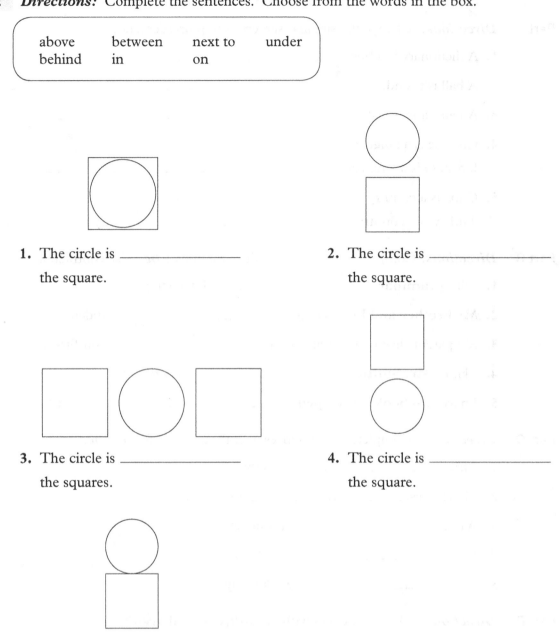

1. The circle is _____ the square.

2. The circle is _____ the square.

3. The circle is _____ the squares.

4. The circle is _____ the square.

5. The circle is _____ the square.

CHAPTER 2 Using *Be* and *Have*

QUIZ 1 **Yes/No Questions with *Be*** (Chart 2-1)

A. *Directions:* Complete the questions with *am, is,* or *are.*

Example: _____Is_____ Beatrice at school today?

1. _____ the students happy?

2. _____ you thirsty?

3. _____ Kamala from Iran?

4. _____ I late?

5. _____ Paris and Madrid cities?

B. *Directions:* Make questions.

Example: A: _Is Martin our teacher ?_
           B: Yes, Martin is our teacher.

1. A: _____
   B: Yes, David is from Toronto.

2. A: _____
   B: Yes, cows are animals.

3. A: _____
   B: Yes, Paulo and Marie are in the library.

4. A: _____
   B: Yes, the weather is cold today.

5. A: _____
   B: Yes, I am a student.

Directions: Make questions and give short answers.

Example: A: <u>*Are the books on the desk?*</u>
B: <u>*Yes, they are.*</u> (*The books are on the desk.*)

1. A: _____
   B: _____ (*I'm homesick.*)

2. A: _____
   B: _____ (*Katya is a nurse.*)

3. A: _____
   B: _____ (*You and Gina are roommates.*)

4. A: _____
   B: _____ (*Rico is not married.*)

5. A: _____
   B: _____ (*My grandparents aren't in Mexico.*)

6. A: _____
   B: _____ (*I'm not a doctor.*)

7. A: _____
   B: _____ (*Mr. Kimura is in his office.*)

8. A: _____
   B: _____ (*We're not tired.*)

9. A: _____
   B: _____ (*Cars are expensive.*)

10. A: _____
    B: _____ (*Julia isn't in the apartment.*)

Directions: Make a yes/no question and a question with ***where*** for each sentence.

Example: Mr. Wu is in class.

    A: _____*Is Mr. Wu in class?*_____

    B: Yes, he is.

    A: _____*Where is Mr. Wu?*_____

    B: In class.

1. Carmen is in New York this week.

    A: _____

    B: Yes, she is.

    A: _____

    B: In New York.

2. Yoko and Rita are at the zoo now.

    A: _____

    B: At the zoo.

    A: _____

    B: Yes, they are.

3. Mr. Morsten is at work today.

    A: _____

    B: Yes, he is.

    A: _____

    B: At work.

4. The train station is on Railroad Avenue.

    A: _____

    B: On Railroad Avenue.

    A: _____

    B: Yes, it is.

5. My sunglasses are in the car.

    A: _____

    B: Yes, they are.

    A: _____

    B: In the car.

Directions: Complete the sentences with ***have*** or ***has***.

Example: Anna _____*has*_____ a cold.

SITUATION: *At the Doctor's Office*

1. Today Dr. Smith is very busy. She _____ many patients in her office.

2. I _____ a toothache.

3. My little brother _____ a sore throat.

4. Mr. and Mrs. Rice _____ stomachaches.

5. Three people _____ the chills.

6. Mrs. Simmons _____ a bad headache.

7. Maria and her sister _____ coughs.

8. You _____ a fever.

9. Jerry _____ a sore back. His wife _____ a sore back, too.

QUIZ 5 **Using *Be* and *Have*** (Charts 1-1, 1-2, and 2-4)

Directions: Choose the correct answer.

Example: They (*are,* (*have*)) a new car.

1. My friend (*is, has*) three dogs. The dogs (*are, have*) very smart.

2. I (*am, have*) a laptop computer. It (*is, has*) new.

3. Mr. Moreno (*is, has*) sick. He (*is, has*) a fever.

4. We always (*are, have*) a lot of homework. We (*are, have*) tired.

5. You (*are, have*) very friendly. You (*are, have*) a lot of friends.

Directions: Complete the sentences with *my, your, his, her, our,* or *their*.

Example: John has on a jacket. _____*His*_____ jacket is green.

1. Miss Chang has on boots. _____ boots are black.

2. Diana and Malika have on skirts. _____ skirts are yellow.

3. You and I have on sweaters. _____ sweaters are blue.

4. John has on jeans. _____ jeans are black.

5. Dimitri and Kostos have on ties. _____ ties are red.

6. You have on a T-shirt. _____ T-shirt is white.

7. Olga and I have on sandals. _____ sandals are brown.

8. Kento and you have on watches. _____ watches are silver.

9. I have on a belt. _____ belt is gray.

10. My parents have on rings. _____ rings are gold.

Directions: Complete the sentences. Use *have* or *has* and *my, your, his, her, our,* or *their*.

Example: Mr. Allen _____*has*_____ a computer. _____*His*_____ computer is fast.

1. You _____ a book. _____ book is interesting.

2. My brother _____ a raincoat. _____ raincoat is waterproof.

3. Paulo and Jarron _____ T-shirts. _____ T-shirts are black.

4. I _____ a backpack. _____ backpack is blue.

5. You and Grace _____ bracelets. _____ bracelets are silver.

6. Ms. Freeman _____ a briefcase. _____ briefcase is brown.

7. My sister and I _____ a car. _____ car is gray.

8. Mr. and Mrs. Ramirez _____ a son. _____ son is two years old.

9. Martin _____ a dictionary. _____ dictionary is yellow.

10. Laura _____ sunglasses. _____ sunglasses are new.

Directions: Complete the sentences with ***this*** or ***that***. The first one is an example.

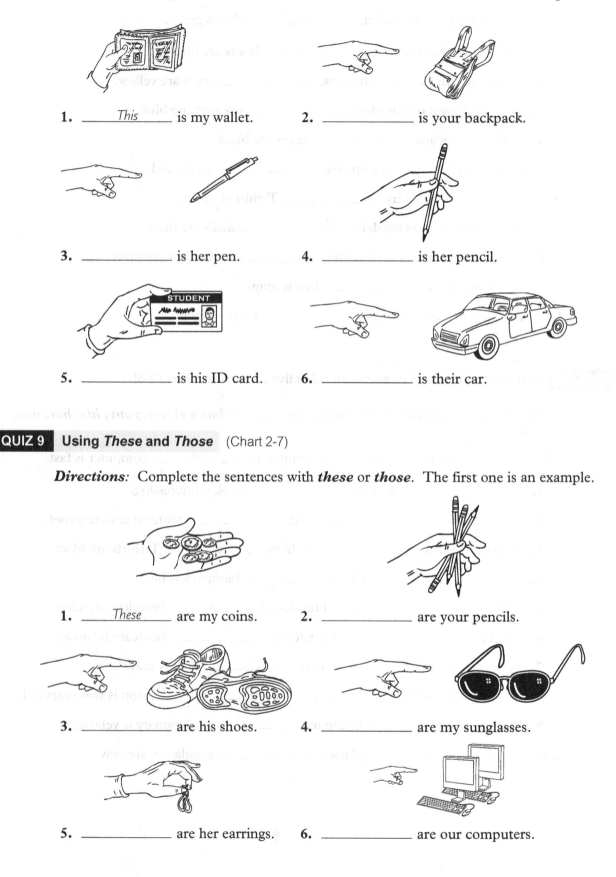

1. ____*This*____ is my wallet.   2. _____ is your backpack.

3. _____ is her pen.   4. _____ is her pencil.

5. _____ is his ID card.   6. _____ is their car.

Directions: Complete the sentences with ***these*** or ***those***. The first one is an example.

1. ____*These*____ are my coins.   2. _____ are your pencils.

3. _____ are his shoes.   4. _____ are my sunglasses.

5. _____ are her earrings.   6. _____ are our computers.

Directions: Choose the correct answer. The first one is an example.

1. (*This*) *These*) watch is expensive. (*That*, *Those*) watches are cheap.
2. (*This*, *These*) T-shirts are dirty. (*That*, *Those*) T-shirt is clean.
3. (*That*, *Those*) car is fast. (*This*, *These*) car is slow.
4. (*That*, *Those*) shoes are new. (*This*, *These*) shoes are old.
5. (*This*, *These*) purse is small. (*That*, *Those*) purse is very big.
6. (*That*, *Those*) dress is ugly. (*This*, *These*) dresses are beautiful.

Directions: Complete the questions. Use *what* or *who* and *is* or *are*.

Example: A: ____*Who is*____ that?
         B: My teacher. She's nice.

1. A: _____ those girls?
   B: My friends. Their names are Alaina and Mia.

2. A: _____ that?
   B: It's my new smart phone.

3. A: _____ those things over there?
   B: They're paperclips.

4. A: _____ that woman?
   B: That's Diane. She's a doctor.

5. A: _____ her name?
   B: Juanita.

6. A: _____ these?
   B: My English books.

7. A: _____ a dictionary?
   B: A dictionary is a book with word meanings.

8. A: _____ your favorite sports stars?
   B: Ichiro Suzuki and David Beckham.

9. A: _____ your address?
   B: 3634 Second Avenue.

10. A: _____ your favorite teacher?
    B: I like Miss Costa. She is very nice.

Directions: Circle the correct completion. The first one is an example.

1. This classroom _____.
   a. has dirty   (b.) is dirty   c. dirty

2. Nadia _____ three notebooks.
   a. has   b. is   c. have

3. Sara is _____ artist.
   a. a   b. an   c. in

4. _____ a student?
   a. Your brother he is   b. Is your brother   c. Your brother he

5. Ella and Jerome have a baby. _____ baby is six weeks old.
   a. They're   b. They   c. Their

6. _____ glasses belong to Rita.
   a. That   b. These   c. This

7. That woman is Ms. Suarez. _____ my teacher.
   a. Is   b. She   c. She's

8. A: _____ that?

   B: It's my ID card.
   a. Who's   b. What's   c. Where is

9. A: Are you a teacher?

   B: No, I _____.
   a. 'm not   b. not   c. aren't

10. This belongs to Tomás. It's _____ briefcase.
    a. he   b. an   c. his

11. A: _____ is the train station?

    B: It's on Main Street.
    a. Who   b. What   c. Where

12. _____ hungry.
    a. We not   b. We're not   c. We isn't

13. _____ Mr. Lim a photographer?
    a. A   b. Are   c. Is

14. A: _____ those people?

    B: My grandparents.
    a. Who are   b. Who's   c. Who

15. Today is Clara's birthday. _____ sixteen years old.
    a. Hers   b. It's   c. She's

16. My brother _____ a new car.
    a. is   b. has   c. have

Directions: Correct the mistakes. The first one is an example.

1. I ~~no~~ thirsty. *I'm not thirsty.*

2. This earrings are beautiful.

3. My father is gardener.

4. What your name?

5. My sister have two children.

6. Natalie not at school today.

7. Ms. Rossi she is your teacher?

8. I have a apple in my backpack.

9. You have a notebook. You notebook is yellow.

10. Roberto and Will are students in my class. They are intelligents.

11. This is'nt my raincoat.

12. Who your favorite teacher is?

13. That ring are expensive.

14. Is the children sick?

15. Michael is three cats.

16. You and your brother is students.

CHAPTER 2–TEST 1

Part A   *Directions:* Make questions and give short answers.

1. A: _____?

   B: _____. (*I am a student.*)

2. A: _____?

   B: _____. (*Selma is not in my class.*)

3. A: _____?

   B: _____. (*My classmates are friendly.*)

4. A: _____?

   B: _____. (*That book is interesting.*)

5. A: _____?

   B: _____. (*Marcos and David are not doctors.*)

Part B   *Directions:* Complete the sentences. Use **have** or **has** and **my**, **your**, **his**, **her**, **our**, or **their**.

1. My brother _____ a job. _____ job is difficult.

2. We _____ dictionaries. _____ dictionaries are heavy.

3. Lynne _____ two children. _____ children are young.

4. My mother and father _____ a car. _____ car isn't new.

5. I _____ three pens. _____ pens have blue ink.

Part C   *Directions:* Circle the correct completion.

1. (*This, These*) is my sweater. (*That, Those*) sweaters belong to my roommate.

2. (*That, Those*) pens belong to Pedro. (*This, These*) are my pens.

3. (*That, Those*) are our desks. (*This, These*) desk belongs to the teacher.

4. (*This, These*) isn't my backpack. (*This, These*) backpack belongs to Jane.

5. (*That, Those*) shirt is dirty. (*That, Those*) shirts are clean.

Part D *Directions:* Circle the correct completion.

1. A: _____ this?
    B: A picture of my apartment.

    a. Who's   b. Who are   c. What's   d. What are

2. A: _____ that?
    B: My grandmother.

    a. Who's   b. Who are   c. What's   d. What are

3. A: _____ your glasses?
    B: In my pocket.

    a. What's   b. What are   c. Where is   d. Where are

4. A: _____ your hometown?
    B: In Canada.

    a. Who's   b. Who are   c. Where is   d. Where are

5. A: _____ those things?
    B: They're batteries.

    a. What's   b. What are   c. Who's   d. Who are

Part E *Directions:* Correct the mistakes.

1. Our teacher no at school today. She have the flu.

2. You have a fever. You head is hot.

3. Where Roberto? Is at school?

4. My book not in my backpack. Where my book is?

5. A: Are you homesick?
    B: Yes, I'm.

CHAPTER 2–TEST 2

Part A   *Directions:* Make questions and give short answers.

1. A: _____?
   B: _____. (*Mrs. Ramirez is sick.*)

2. A: _____?
   B: _____. (*Joe is not from London.*)

3. A: _____?
   B: _____. (*Those shoes are comfortable.*)

4. A: _____?
   B: _____. (*Quebec is not in the United States.*)

5. A: _____?
   B: _____. (*You and your sister are in the same class.*)

Part B   *Directions:* Complete the sentences. Use **have** or **has** and **my, your, his, her, our,** or **their**.

1. I _____ two notebooks. _____ notebooks are at home.

2. You and I _____ backpacks. _____ backpacks are full of books.

3. You _____ three classes. _____ classes are interesting.

4. Flora _____ new earrings. _____ earrings are gold.

5. Yoko and Ken _____ a bird. _____ bird is yellow.

Part C   *Directions:* Circle the correct completion.

1. (*That, Those*) is my umbrella. (*This, These*) umbrellas belong to my classmates.

2. (*This, These*) is our house. (*That, Those*) house belongs to Mr. and Mrs. Palmer.

3. (*That, Those*) jackets belong to Don. (*This, These*) is my jacket.

4. (*This, These*) aren't my boots. (*This, These*) boots belong to Eva.

5. (*That, Those*) books belong to Max. (*This, These*) are my books.

Part D *Directions:* Circle the correct completion.

1. A: This photo is interesting. _____ those people?
   B: My cousins.

   a. Who's   b. Who are   c. Where is   d. Where are

2. A: _____ they?
   B: At the zoo in Cairo.

   a. Who's   b. Who are   c. Where is   d. Where are

3. A: _____ Cairo?
   B: It's in Egypt.

   a. Who's   b. Who are   c. Where is   d. Where are

4. A: _____ this?
   B: I'm not sure. That man isn't in my family.

   a. What's   b. What are   c. Who's   d. Who are

5. A: _____ that?
   B: It's a turtle.

   a. What's   b. What are   c. Who's   d. Who are

Part E *Directions:* Correct the mistakes.

1. Mr. Chang have a blue jacket.

2. Who your English teacher is?

3. Carlos and Maria has a house in Mexico. They house is beautiful.

4. This are your sunglasses. They are n't my sunglasses.

5. Where your apartment? Is on Grand Street?

CHAPTER 3 Using the Simple Present

QUIZ 1 **Simple Present Tense Form** (Chart 3-1)

Directions: Complete the sentences with *like* or *likes*.

Example: Ali _____ *likes* _____ ice cream.

1. I _____ dancing.

2. My sister _____ movies.

3. Meg and I _____ speaking English.

4. You _____ cars.

5. Ivan _____ swimming.

6. You and your brother _____ basketball.

7. Mr. Jeffries _____ pizza.

8. Cats _____ sleeping.

9. Alexandra _____ hamburgers.

10. Teenagers _____ cell phones.

QUIZ 2 **Simple Present Tense Form** (Chart 3-1)

Directions: Choose the correct completions. The first one is an example.

SITUATION: *Weekday Habits*

My brother (*eat, eats*) breakfast at 6:00 every morning. He (*do, does*) exercises
at 6:30. I (*eat, eats*) breakfast at 7:00. I (*watch, watches*) TV at 7:30. My brother
(*walk, walks*) to school with me at 8:00. Class (*begin, begins*) at 8:30. I (*go, goes*) to
the cafeteria at 12:30 for lunch. My friends (*eat, eats*) lunch with me. My brother
(*study, studies*) English every afternoon. I (*talk, talks*) to my friends. My brother and
I (*walk, walks*) home together at 4:00.

A. Directions: Complete the sentences in the chart. Use each frequency adverb from the box once. The first one is an example.

| always | never | ✓ often | seldom/rarely | sometimes | usually |

	Mon.	Tues.	Wed.	Thurs.	Fri.	Sat.	Sun.
1. Igor ___often___ watches TV in the morning.	📺		📺		📺	📺	📺
2. Rosa _____ watches TV in the morning.	📺	📺	📺	📺	📺	📺	📺
3. Jacques _____ watches TV in the morning.	📺	📺	📺		📺	📺	📺
4. Irina _____ watches TV in the morning.							
5. Alex _____ watches TV in the morning.	📺		📺		📺		
6. Will _____ watches TV in the morning.	📺						

B. Directions: Choose the correct completion.

Example: Juan wakes up at 7:30 every morning. He (⟨always,⟩ often) wakes up at 7:30.

1. Steve plays computer games on Fridays, Saturdays and Sundays. He (*always, sometimes*) plays computer games.

2. Yelena eats meat once a week. She (*usually, seldom*) eats meat.

3. Grammar class begins at 9:00 every morning. It (*sometimes, never*) begins at 10:00.

4. Ali uses his cell phone twenty times every day. He (*often, rarely*) uses his cell phone.

5. Winnie is late for class every day. She is (*usually, always*) late for class.

A. *Directions:* Complete the sentences. Use *once*, *twice*, or *three times*, etc., plus the appropriate time words.

Example: Sonya sees her grandparents on Sunday every week.

Sonya sees her grandparents _____*once a week*_____.

1. Max sees his cousin on December 25th every year.

   Max sees his cousin _____.

2. Abdul brushes his teeth at 7:00, 1:00, and 9:30 every day.

   Abdul brushes his teeth _____.

3. Mr. Yang pays bills on the 1st and the 15th of every month.

   Mr. Yang pays bills _____.

4. Maria does exercises on Monday, Tuesday, Friday, and Saturday every week.

   Maria does exercises _____.

5. Andy talks to Pippa at 8:00, 10:00, 12:00, 3:00, 6:00, and 9:00 every day.

   Andy talks to Pippa _____.

B. *Directions:* Add the frequency adverbs in italics to the sentences.

Example: always   Anna is ∧ hungry by lunchtime.
                        always

1. *usually*   Marcos is in the cafeteria at 12:00.

2. *sometimes*   Gloria stays at school in the afternoon.

3. *often*   I am at home by three o'clock.

4. *always*   My sisters are at home in the evening.

5. *never*   They go to bed late.

Directions: Finish the sentences. Add ***-s*** or ***-es*** to the verbs. The first one is an example.

SITUATION: *Mr. Landry's Busy Day*

Every day, Mr. Landry . . .

1. *wash*   <u>   washes   </u> his clothes.

2. *sit*   <u>   </u> in a chair.

3. *push*   <u>   </u> a shopping cart.

4. *kiss*   <u>   </u> his wife.

5. *take*   <u>   </u> a shower.

6. *fix*   <u>   </u> a cup of tea.

7. *watch*   <u>   </u> TV.

8. *speak*   <u>   </u> English.

9. *talk*   <u>   </u> to his son.

10. *brush*   <u>   </u> his teeth.

11. *teach*   <u>   </u> a class.

Directions: Complete each sentence with the simple present form of a verb from the box. The first one is an example.

> buy   cry   enjoy   fly   pay   play   say   stay   study   try   ✓worry

1. My mother always _____*worries*_____ about me.

2. Hiro is a pilot. He _____ a plane.

3. Elena goes to class early in the morning. She usually _____ to leave her house by 7:00.

4. James goes shopping at the college bookstore twice a year. He _____ his school supplies and books there.

5. Ivan is a good student. He _____ at the library every night.

6. Franco _____ music. He listens to music every evening.

7. Mrs. Bendana is a mother. She _____ home and takes care of her children.

8. Mathieu _____ for his books and supplies every year. They are expensive.

9. Miriam loves music. She _____ the piano very well.

10. Anne is a teacher. She _____ "Good Morning!" to her class every day.

11. Eva is a quiet baby. She rarely _____.

Directions: Complete the sentences with the words in parentheses. Use the simple present tense.

Example: We seldom (*go*) _____*go*_____ to the movies.

1. Mrs. Garcia usually (*go*) _____ shopping on Saturday.

2. Rosa (*do*) _____ her homework on Sunday night.

3. My friend and I (*go*) _____ to the beach every weekend.

4. My classmates usually (*have*) _____ coffee together in the afternoon.

5. Nora and Anita (*do*) _____ exercises in the morning.

6. My father rarely (*have*) _____ time for breakfast.

7. Henri (*go*) _____ to the library at 7:00 every evening.

8. My sister always (*have*) _____ a lot of homework.

9. We never (*do*) _____ our laundry on Sunday.

10. Fatima sometimes (*go*) _____ to the bank after school.

Directions: Complete the sentences with the words in parentheses. Use the simple present tense. The first one is an example.

Yuko (*study, seldom*) _*seldom studies*_ in the evening. She (*worry, never*)

_____ about her grades. She (*invite, often*) _____ her friends to her

house. Spencer and I (*spend, usually*) _____ our evenings with her. Yuko

(*have*) _____ a computer in her room. She (*play, sometimes*) _____

computer games. Spencer and Yuko (*surf, often*) _____ the Internet on

her computer. Spencer (*be, always*) _____ hungry by 9:00 P.M. He

(*go*) _____ into the kitchen to make snacks. Then we (*watch, usually*)

_____ a movie together. Spencer and I (*say*) _____ goodnight to

Yuko at midnight.

A. *Directions:* Make complete sentences. Pay attention to the final *-s* ending on singular verbs.

Example: Micah \ want \ watch a movie. _____Micah wants to watch a movie._____

1. Natalie \ need \ buy vegetables _____

2. I \ want \ go \ to the library _____

3. My dad \ like \ read on the Internet _____

4. Felix and you \ need \ study _____

5. Dr. Swanson \ like \ help people _____

B. *Directions:* Correct the mistakes.

Example: Micah wants⌃watch a movie.
$\qquad\qquad\qquad\quad$ to

1. I needs to find my keys.

2. Francisco want to watch the news on TV.

3. Sam likes to answers questions in class.

4. Anna needs help her mother today.

5. My brother and I likes to eat ice cream.

QUIZ 10 **The Simple Present: Negative** (Chart 3-8)

Directions: Use the words in *italics* to make negative sentences. Use contractions.

Example: have, not John _doesn't have_ a backpack. He carries a briefcase.

1. *take, not*   Rita _____ baths. She takes showers.

2. *know, not*   I _____ that man. Who is he?

3. *live, not*   Ali and Sam _____ in an apartment. They have a house.

4. *want, not*   Bob _____ anything to eat. He's not hungry.

5. *drive, not*   I _____ a car. I ride a bicycle.

6. *like, not*   You _____ cats. You like dogs.

7. *work, not*   My cell phone _____. I need to buy a new one.

8. *study, not*   Kristof _____ on weekends. He rests.

9. *have, not*   Riyadh _____ cold weather. It is usually hot.

10. *do, not*   My brother and I _____ exercises every day. We do them twice a week.

The Simple Present: Negative (Charts 1-6, 1-7, and 3-8)

Directions: Choose the correct verb.

Example: Ed (*is not,* (*does not*)) speak Spanish.

1. Ms. Roy (*is not, does not*) teach history.
2. We (*are not, do not*) eat breakfast at home.
3. Marie and Vera (*are not, do not*) in the classroom.
4. Tito (*is not, does not*) play tennis.
5. It (*is not, does not*) hot here in January.
6. Frogs (*are not, do not*) live in houses.
7. Emma (*is not, does not*) have any children.
8. I (*am not, do not*) a dancer.
9. It (*is not, does not*) rain a lot here in October.
10. Shoe stores (*are not, do not*) sell ice cream.

Review (Charts 3-1 → 3-8)

Directions: Complete the sentences with the words in parentheses. Use the simple present tense. The first one is an example.

1. Ben (*try*) _____ *tries* _____ to come to class on time, but he (*come, often*) _____
   late.

2. Ali and Samir (*have, not*) _____ pets. Anya (*have*) _____
   a cat and two dogs. She (*wash*) _____ the dogs once a month. She (*wash,*
   never) _____ the cat. Cats (*like, not*) _____ to take baths.

3. You (*have, not*) _____ a fever. You (*need, not*)_____ to go to the
   doctor.

4. My sister (*play*) _____ tennis every afternoon. She (*do, not*) _____
   her homework.

A. *Directions:* Choose the correct answer.

Example: Do you send your parents an email every day?

a. Yes, I send (b.) Yes, I do.

1. Does Kenji play baseball?   a. No, he don't.   b. No, he doesn't.
2. Do Mr. and Mrs. Rivera speak Spanish?   a. Yes, they do.   b. Yes, they speak.
3. Does Martina like coffee?   a. No, she doesn't.   b. No, she isn't.
4. Do you have a computer?   a. Yes, I have.   b. Yes, I do.
5. Do Max and Peter have a dog?   a. Yes, he does.   b. Yes, they do.

B. *Directions:* Correct the mistakes.

Example: Does Aidan ~~has~~ a brother?   *have*

1. Does Petra and Ivan need help?
2. Do you your homework every day?
3. Does he speaks Japanese?
4. Do they I like Chinese food?
5. Does is Katya take a nap in the afternoon?

Directions: Complete the questions in the simple present. Use the words in *italics*.
Then complete the short answers.

Example: *they, have*   A: _____*Do they have*_____ enough money for the bus?

                   B: Yes, ___*they do*___ .

1. *you, play*   A: _____ soccer?

                        B: Yes, _____.

2. *Maria, be*   A: _____ a teacher?

                        B: No, _____.

3. *Rob, have*   A: _____ a new car?

                        B: No, _____.

4. *Paulo and Lana, live*   A: _____ in a house?

                        B: Yes, _____.

5. *it, snow*   A: _____ a lot in January?

                        B: Yes, _____.

6. *it, be*   A: _____ cold in August?

                        B: No, _____.

7. *you, have*   A: _____ a cat?

                        B: No, _____.

8. *Amanda, wear*   A: _____ dresses at home?

                        B: No, _____.

9. *they, be*   A: _____ from Spain?

                        B: Yes, _____.

10. *your friends, walk*   A: _____ to school?

                        B: No, _____.

Directions: Make questions with *where* or *what*.

Example: A: _____ *Where do you usually swim?* _____

B: At the lake. (*I usually swim at the lake.*)

1. A: _____

B: In Seattle. (*I live in Seattle.*)

2. A: _____

B: Coffee. (*Bonnie likes coffee.*)

3. A: _____

B: Money. (*They need money.*)

4. A: _____

B: To the zoo. (*Vinesh often goes to the zoo.*)

5. A: _____

B: Math. (*Jared teaches Math.*)

6. A: _____

B: At the market. (*Angela buys vegetables at the market.*)

7. A: _____

B: Some candy. (*Makda and Delina want some candy.*)

8. A: _____

B: At the hospital. (*Artur works at the hospital.*)

9. A: _____

B: On the table. (*I always put flowers on the table.*)

10. A: _____

B: A sandwich. (*Todd usually eats a sandwich for lunch.*)

(Chart 3-10 and 3-11)

Directions: Make questions with ***where, what, when,*** or ***what time.***

Example: A: ___*When/What time does Luis eat lunch?*___

B: At 12:30. (*Luis eats lunch at 12:30.*)

1. A: _____

   B: At school. (*I play basketball at school.*)

2. A: _____

   B: At 8:30. (*The girls go to bed at 8:30.*)

3. A: _____

   B: Some ice cream. (*Waleed wants some ice cream.*)

4. A: _____

   B: At 9:00 P.M. (*The restaurant closes at 9:00 P.M.*)

5. A: _____

   B: English. (*They study English.*)

6. A: _____

   B: In the closet. (*He hangs his coat in the closet.*)

7. A: _____

   B: Between 8:00 and 10:00. (*Karl usually does his homework between 8:00 and 10:00.*)

8. A: _____

   B: At the library. (*Tara often studies at the library.*)

9. A: _____

   B: Around 6:00. (*I usually cook dinner around 6:00.*)

10. A: _____

   B: At four o'clock. (*Lisa usually goes home at four o'clock.*)

Directions: Circle the correct completion.

Example: A: What time _____ eat breakfast?

       (a.) do you   b. are you   c. you

        B: At seven.

1. A: Where _____ to school?

        a. he goes   b. he go   c. does he go

   B: City College.

2. A: What _____ in the evenings?

        a. is she do   b. does she do   c. does she

   B: She stays home.

   A: _____ she study English?

        a. Is   b. Do   c. Does

   B: No, she _____. She watches TV.

        a. doesn't   b. don't   c. isn't

3. A: When do _____ to the library?

        a. usually they go   b. they usually go   c. they go usually

   B: After dinner.

   A: _____ they at the library now?

        a. Are   b. Does   c. Do

   B: Yes, they _____.

        a. do   b. are   c. does

4. A: _____ spend a lot of time cooking?

        a. Do you   b. Are you   c. You are

   B: Yes, I _____.

        a. am   b. spend   c. do

   A: What _____ like to cook?

        a. you are   b. do you   c. are you

   B: Chinese food.

Directions: Complete the questions. Use *is*, *are*, *does*, or *do*.

Example: What _____*do*_____ Salina and Martin do in the evening?

1. What _____ your name?

2. Where _____ you live?

3. _____ you a student?

4. Where _____ your school?

5. What time _____ class begin?

6. _____ your sister in your class?

7. _____ she have a job?

8. Where _____ your sister work?

9. When _____ your classmates go home?

10. _____ they study at home every evening?

QUIZ 19 **Chapter Review**

Directions: Correct the mistakes. The first one is an example.

     have

1. Bill doesn't ~~has~~ a raincoat.

2. We speak always English in class.

3. I usually study at home. My friend studys at the library.

4. A: Do you want a new car?
   B: Yes, I want.

5. Is your sister have a computer at home?

6. We no need new clothes.

7. My roommate does'nt drink coffee.

8. Ellen is married. She's have a diamond ring.

9. Does Franco plays soccer every weekend?

10. What time you go to school?

11. Eli don't drive to school every morning.

CHAPTER 3–TEST 1

Part A   *Directions:* Complete the sentences with the verb in *italics*. Use the verb for both sentences. Use the simple present tense.

1. *speak*   Hamid _____ Arabic and English. I _____ Chinese and English.

2. *go*   Maria _____ shopping once a month. Her roommates _____ shopping once a week.

3. *buy*   Yoko _____ a lot of clothes. Tina _____ a lot of books.

4. *study*   We _____ at the library. Alan _____ in his room.

5. *teach*   Mr. Diaz and Ms. Kim _____ history. Mrs. Lee _____ math.

Part B   *Directions:* Complete the sentences with the words in parentheses. Use the simple present tense.

1. Omar (*work*) _____ at a restaurant every night. He (*leave, not*) _____ the restaurant until 1:00 A.M., and he (*get, rarely*) _____ to sleep before 2:00 A.M. He (*be, usually*) _____ sleepy in class. Omar (*have, not*) _____ time to work late and study, too.

2. My parents (*stay*) _____ at home every evening. They (*go, not*) _____ to movies or concerts. I (*like, not*) _____ to stay at home. My friends and I (*go, usually*) _____ out in the evening. We (*have, always*) _____ a lot of fun.

Part C   *Directions:* Correct the mistakes.

1. Marta miss her brothers. They lives in Venezuela.

2. Quan doesn't has a car. He takes usually the bus.

3. What time is Teresa leave home every morning?

4. Ali enjoy soccer, but he don't like baseball.

5. I no like pizza. Are you like pizza?

Part D   *Directions:* Circle the correct completions.

1. A: _____ does Mrs. Miller teach?

    a. What time   b. Where   c. What

   B: At the local high school.

2. A: _____ does Matt have breakfast?

    a. When   b. Where   c. What

   B: Around seven.

3. A: Where _____ go after class?

    a. your brothers   b. do your brothers   c. are your brothers

   B: To work.

4. A: _____ Anna do homework every day?

    a. Is   b. Does   c. Do

   B: No, she _____.

    a. doesn't   b. don't   c. isn't

5. A: When _____ get up in the morning?

    a usually do you   b. are you usually   c. do you usually

   B: At seven-thirty.

6. A: _____ your mother a teacher?

    a. Is   b. Does   c. Are

   B: Yes, she _____.

    a. is   b. does   c. are

7. A: _____ your mother and father live in an apartment?

    a. Are   b. Do   c. Does

   B: Yes, they _____.

    a. are   b. do   c. does

CHAPTER 3–TEST 2

Part A *Directions:* Complete the sentences with the verb in *italics*. Use the verb for both sentences. Use the simple present tense.

1. *work* My cousin _____ at a restaurant. I _____ at a hotel.

2. *have* Jan _____ coffee every morning. Anna and Sue _____ coffee once a week.

3. *catch* We _____ the bus at 8:15. Olga _____ the bus at 8:30.

4. *carry* Carlos _____ his books in a briefcase. Jed _____ his books in a backpack.

5. *play* Jay and I _____ soccer. Matt _____ basketball.

Part B *Directions:* Complete the sentences with the words in parentheses. Use the simple present tense.

My name (*be*) _____ Adriana. I (*live*) _____ with my parents
1 2

and my brothers. We (*live*) _____ in the United States. My grandmother
3

(*live, not*) _____ with us. She (*live*) _____ in Mexico. She
4 5

(*write, always*) _____ letters to us. We (*call, usually*) _____ her once a
6 7

week. We (*talk, often*) _____ for hours. My brothers and I (*miss*) _____
8 9

our grandmother. She (*miss*) _____ her grandchildren.
10

Part C *Directions:* Correct the mistakes.

1. Diane talks on her cell phone in her car. I'm never use my cell phone in my car.

2. What time you go to bed every nights?

3. Ingrid don't like school. She skips often class.

4. Mark no wants a new coat. He isn't need a coat.

5. A: Are you know Jim Anderson?

   B: I'm not sure. Does he has blond hair?

Part D   *Directions:* Circle the correct completions.

1. A: _____ do you wear to school?

   a. What time   b. Where   c. What

   B: T-shirts and jeans.

2. A: _____ does Mike go to school?

   a. When   b. Where   c. What

   B: Lynndale College.

3. A: _____ does Diane study?

   a. What time   b. Where   c. What

   B: Art history.

4. A: What _____ like to watch on TV?

   a. do your parents   b. are your parents   c. your parents

   B: The news.

5. A: Does _____ her homework every day?

   a. Laura   b. Laura do   c. Laura does

   B: Yes, _____.

   a. does   b. she do   c. she does

6. A: _____ their father a bus driver?

   a. Is   b. Does   c. Are

   B: No, _____.

   a. he doesn't   b. they're not   c. he's not

7. A: _____ your roommates enjoy sports?

   a. Are   b. Do   c. Does

   B: No, they _____.

   a. aren't   b. don't   c. doesn't

CHAPTER 4 Using the Present Progressive

QUIZ 1 *Be + -ing* (Chart 4-1)

Directions: Complete the sentences with the correct form of *be* (*am*, *is*, or *are*).

Example: Ivan and I _____*are*_____ studying English.

1. Nadia _____ writing an email.

2. Masasko and Hyeri _____ watching a movie.

3. I _____ thinking in English.

4. You _____ looking out the window.

5. Giovanni _____ reading on the Internet.

6. My parents _____ helping my grandmother.

7. It _____ raining outside.

8. My classmates and I _____ starting Chapter 4.

9. We _____ writing our answers.

10. I _____ finishing Quiz 1.

QUIZ 2 **Spelling of *-ing*** (Chart 4-2)

Directions: Write the *-ing* form of the given verbs. The first one is an example.

1. run   ____*running*____   9. read   _____

2. fix   _____   10. brush   _____

3. sleep   _____   11. put   _____

4. stop   _____   12. make   _____

5. get   _____   13. swim   _____

6. drive   _____   14. study   _____

7. buy   _____   15. smile   _____

8. count   _____   16. play   _____

Directions: Complete each sentence with the present progressive form of the verb in *italics*.

Example: *sing* The birds ___*are singing*___ .

SITUATION: *At the Park*

The park is very busy today. Right now. . .

1. *shine*   The sun _____ .

2. *walk*   Many people _____ .

3. *fish*   A man _____ in the lake.

4. *have*   We _____ a picnic.

5. *sit*   Ms. Wauters _____ on a bench.

6. *climb*   Some boys _____ trees.

7. *play*   Zana and Ella _____ tennis.

8. *swim*   You _____ in the lake.

9. *ride*   I _____ my bike.

10. *bark*   A dog _____ .

Directions: Complete the negative and affirmative sentences. Use the present progressive form of the verb in *italics*.

Example: *sleep, not* Carlos ___isn't sleeping___.

          watch He _'s watching TV_.

1. *wear, not*   Emiko _____ a dress.

   wear   She _____ jeans.

2. *eat, not*   Soon-Yi and Jun _____ dinner at home.

   eat   They _____ at a restaurant.

3. *drink, not*   I _____ coffee.

   drink   I _____ tea.

4. *walk, not*   Alex _____ to school.

   ride   He _____ his bicycle.

5. *fly, not*   The bird _____ now.

   sleep   It _____.

6. *clean, not*   My sisters _____ their rooms.

   watch   They _____ a movie.

7. *surf, not*   We _____ the Internet.

   use   We _____ the computer to do our homework.

8. *sit, not*   Alicia _____ at her desk.

   run   She _____ in the park.

9. *pay, not*   You _____ attention.

   send   You _____ a text message.

10. *buy, not*   Uncle Ted _____ a new car.

    drive   He _____ his old car.

The Present Progressive: Yes/No Questions (Chart 4-4)

Directions: Make questions and short answers. Use the present progressive.

Example: A: _____Are your parents driving_____ to Chicago?

B: Yes, _____they are_____. (*My parents are driving to Chicago.*)

1. A: _____ a history class?

   B: Yes, _____. (*Max is taking a history class.*)

2. A: _____ at the library?

   B: No, _____. (*Tito and Anna aren't studying at the library.*)

3. A: _____ in her office?

   B: No, _____. (*Ms. Park isn't working in her office.*)

4. A: _____ outside?

   B: Yes, _____. (*It's snowing outside.*)

5. A: _____ the correct answers?

   B: Yes, _____. (*I am writing the correct answers.*)

The Present Progressive: Questions with *Where, What,* and *Why* (Chart 4-4)

Directions: Make questions with *where, what,* and *why.* Use the present progressive.

Example: A: _____What is Matt reading?_____

B: A magazine. (*Matt is reading a magazine.*)

1. A: _____

   B: At the library. (*Abdul is studying at the library.*)

2. A: _____

   B: Because it's raining outside. (*Kate is wearing a raincoat because it's raining outside.*)

3. A: _____

   B: A pizza. (*I'm making a pizza.*)

4. A: _____

   B: Next to Pedro. (*Rita is standing next to Pedro.*)

5. A: _____

   B: Because I'm hungry. (*I'm eating ice cream because I'm hungry.*)

Directions: Make questions. Give short answers to yes/no questions. Use the present progressive.

Examples: A: <u> Are your parents driving </u> to Chicago?

       B: Yes, <u>   they are   </u>. (*My parents are driving to Chicago.*)

       A: <u> What is Matt reading? </u>

       B: A magazine. (*Matt is reading a magazine.*)

1. A: _____ a cooking class?

    B: Yes, _____. (*Maria and Paulo are taking a cooking class.*)

2. A: _____ lunch?

    B: No, _____. (*I'm not eating lunch.*)

3. A: _____

    B: In the living room. (*Cinda is watching TV in the living room.*)

4. A: _____ soccer?

    B: Yes, _____. (*Anna is playing soccer.*)

5. A: _____?

    B: No, _____. (*The sun isn't shining.*)

6. A: _____

    B: Because it's Mika's birthday. (*They are eating cake because it's Mika's birthday.*)

7. A: _____

    B: His text messages. (*Evan is reading his text messages.*)

8. A: _____ on a vacation?

    B: Yes, _____. (*We are going on a vacation.*)

9. A: _____

    B: Because he has an exam. (*Alex is studying because he has an exam.*)

10. A: _____

     B: The laundry. (*Sherry is doing the laundry.*)

Directions: Complete the sentences with the correct form of the words in parentheses. Use the simple present or the present progressive.

Example: I usually (*walk*) _____walk_____ to school, but today I (*ride*) ___am riding___ the bus.

1. Please be quiet. The baby (*sleep*) _____ now. She (*sleep*) _____ for two hours every afternoon.

2. A: Look outside. It (*snow*) _____!

   B: (*it, snow*) _____ a lot here in the winter?

   A: No, not a lot.

3. A: Where's Kathy? She usually (*sit*) _____ at this desk. She (*sit, not*) _____ at her desk right now.

   B: I see Kathy. She is over there. She (*talk*) _____ to Samir.

4. I (*get*) _____ ready to walk to school now. It (*rain, not*) _____ outside right now, so I (*wear, not*) _____ my raincoat.

Directions: Complete the sentences with **Do, Does, Is,** or **Are**.

Example: ___Is___ it raining now?

   ___Do___ I need my umbrella?

SITUATION: *Your English Class*

1. _____ you like English?

2. _____ the classroom large?

3. _____ the students in your class usually study hard?

4. _____ your teacher talking now?

5. _____ the class interesting?

6. _____ the students listening carefully?

7. _____ they have a test today?

8. _____ your school have many English classes?

9. _____ your grammar getting better?

10. _____ your teacher help you learn?

Directions: Complete the sentences. Use *am, is, are, do,* or *does.*

Example: __Do__ Toshi and Ali do their homework in the library? __Are__ they at the library now?

1. Where _____ Annie? _____ she riding her bicycle in the park?

2. _____ you carry your books to school in a backpack?

3. The sun _____ shining. Why _____ you carrying an umbrella?

4. _____ Ms. Anderson usually drive her car to school?

5. Why _____ Otto and Hans making so much noise? What _____ they doing? _____ they trying to move some furniture?

6. Where _____ your uncle work?

7. Why _____ that cat eating my ice-cream cone? _____ I dreaming? _____ I awake or asleep?

8. _____ Julia and Catherine see each other often? _____ they meeting each other today?

Directions: Complete the sentences. Use the simple present or the present progressive form of the verbs in parentheses.

Example: I (*hear*) _____*hear*_____ a noise in the kitchen. Someone (*take*) _____*is taking*_____ food out of the refrigerator.

1. Luis (*talk*) _____ to Rosa right now. Luis (*like*) _____ Rosa. He (*think*) _____ that she's beautiful.

2. David (*need*) _____ some things for school, so he's at the store right now. He (*buy*) _____ new notebooks and a pen.

3. Alessandro and Michaela (*speak*) _____ Italian to each other right now. Carlo (*know*) _____ Italian too. He (*understand*) _____ their conversation.

4. Tina (*eat*) _____ pizza right now. I (*want*) _____ some pizza too.

A. ***Directions:*** Choose the correct verb.

Example: I'm (*hearing,* listening to) my voicemail. I have two messages.

1. Bob likes sports. He (*sees, watches*) tennis and baseball games for hours every weekend.

2. Look at this picture. What do you (*see, watch*)?

3. I'm (*looking at, watching*) page 97 in my dictionary. I want to know how to spell *giraffe.*

4. Lee wants to learn grammar. He pays attention in class. He (*hears, listens to*) the teacher.

5. Oh no! I (*hear, listen to*) a noise outside the window. What is it?

B. ***Directions:*** Use a word or phrase from the box to complete each sentence. Use each word or phrase one time only. The first one is an example.

> music   a map   friends   a phone   a movie   ✓their parents

1. Babies look at ___their parents___ and smile.

2. She hears _____ in the restaurant.

3. Mark often sees _____ on the bus to school.

4. I listen to _____ on my earphones.

5. We usually look at _____ when we travel.

6. I watch _____ on my computer every weekend.

Directions: Complete the sentences with *think that* or *think about*. Use the simple present or the present progressive.

Example: Some students _____*think that*_____ Grammar class is fun.

1. Peter is hungry, so right now he _____ food.

2. I'm sitting in the cafeteria, but I'm not eating. I _____ the food in the cafeteria is bad.

3. Paulo misses his family. He often _____ his brothers and sisters in Brazil.

4. Tim _____ cars right now. He _____ cars every day. He loves cars.

5. My parents _____ the Internet is useful.

6. Right now, Makda and Andy _____ their vacation. They _____ Mexico is a great place to visit.

7. I like Chris. I _____ Chris right now. I _____ he's nice.

QUIZ 14 **Chapter Review**

Directions: Complete the sentences. Use the simple present or the present progressive form of the verbs in parentheses.

Example: I (*hear*) _____*hear*_____ a noise in the kitchen. Someone (*cook*) _____*is cooking*_____.

1. Matt and I (*sit*) _____ in our classroom right now. We (*wait*) _____ for our teacher. Matt and I (*talk, usually*) _____ to our classmates before class, but Matt (*talk, not*) _____ now. He (*think*) _____ about his physics test. Matt (*like*) _____ physics, but he (*think*) _____ that physics tests are difficult.

2. Today is Sunday. Right now, Patricia (*relax*) _____ in the park with her cousins. They (*have*) _____ a picnic. Patricia is happy. She (*love*) _____ picnics with her family.

Directions: Correct the mistakes.

watching

Example: Maria is ~~looking at~~ the news on TV.

1. I'm hungry now. I'm wanting a pizza.

2. Rosita doesn't reading right now. She's writting in her notebook.

3. You are doing your homework every day.

4. Joe is in his room now. He's listening music.

5. Is the sun shinning now?

6. That story is not true. I'm not believing it.

7. What the girls are doing right now?

8. Right now I watch a football game on TV. I'm think that football is exciting.

Directions: Circle the correct completions. The first one is an example.

1. Abdul _____ soccer at the park right now.

   a. playing   (b.) is playing   c. plays

2. My clothes are old. I _____ new jeans and T-shirts.

   a. needing   b. am needing   c. need

3. Olga _____ dinner right now. She's outside with her children.

   a. isn't cooking   b. doesn't cook   c. not cooking

4. Ivan often _____ his friends in his country. He wants to see them.

   a. thinks   b. is thinking   c. thinks about

5. This ice cream is delicious. It _____ very good.

   a. is tastes   b. tastes   c. is tasting

6. Let's go outside. It _____ now.

   a. isn't rain   b. doesn't rain   c. isn't raining

7. Risa and Tomo usually _____ the bus to school at eight o'clock.

   a. take   b. taking   c. are taking

8. _____ the people in this city are friendly?

   a. Are you thinking   b. Do you think   c. Do you think about

9. A: What _____? B: I'm baking a cake.

   a. are you doing   b. do you do   c. you do

10. Look at that tree. _____ a squirrel in it?

    a. Are you seeing   b. Do you see   c. Do you watch

11. Anna doesn't like cars. She _____ cars are boring.

    a. is thinking that   b. thinks about   c. thinks that

CHAPTER 4—TEST 1

Part A *Directions:* Complete the sentences. Use the present progressive form of the verbs in parentheses.

1. I (*talk, not*) _____ to my classmates now. I (*read*) _____ my book.

2. The baby (*cry, not*) _____ now. She (*laugh*) _____ .

3. The boys (*run*) _____ in the park now. They (*ride, not*) _____ their bikes.

4. It (*rain, not*) _____ now. It (*snow*) _____ .

5. We (*eat, not*) _____ breakfast. We (*drink*) _____ tea.

Part B *Directions:* Complete the sentences. Use the simple present or the present progressive form of the verbs in parentheses.

1. Ben and Carlos (*go*) _____ on a picnic every weekend. They usually (*play*) _____ games at their picnics.

2. Diana (*be, not*) _____ here because she (*work*) _____ right now. She (*work*) _____ at a restaurant every Saturday. The restaurant (*be*) _____ nice, so Diana (*like*) _____ her job.

3. Ali (*want*) _____ a new jacket, so right now he (*shop*) _____ at a store downtown. He (*look*) _____ for a dark brown jacket.

Part C   *Directions:* Circle the correct completions.

1. A: _____ Alex doing his homework?

    a. Are   b. Is   c. Does

   B: No, he _____.

    a. not   b. isn't   c. doesn't

2. A: Does Olga usually _____ English at home?

    a. speak   b. speaks   c. speaking

   B: Yes, she _____.

    a. is   b. is speaking   c. does

3. A: _____ Anna and Hans helping each other?

    a. Are   b. Is   c. Do

   B: No, they _____.

    a. not   b. aren't   c. don't

4. A: Do your parents _____ your new friend?

    a. likes   b. like   c. liking

   B: Yes, they _____.

    a. like   b. are   c. do

5. A: Why _____ smiling?

    a. you are   b. are you   c. do you

   B: Because _____ funny.

    a. you are   b. are you   c. do you

Part D   *Directions:* Correct the errors.

1. It isn't cold outside today. You aren't needing your coat.

2. Pablo doesn't sleep right now. He's listening to music.

3. Alice is upstairs now. She getting ready for school.

4. Do you see that girl over there? Are you knowing her name?

5. My parents taking a walk right now.

CHAPTER 4—TEST 2

Part A   *Directions:* Complete the sentences. Use the present progressive form of the verbs in parentheses.

1. Kenji *(wash)* _____ his face right now. He *(brush, not)*
   _____ his teeth.

2. It's lunchtime now, so my classmates and I *(sit, not)* _____ in class.
   We're outside. We *(enjoy)* _____ the beautiful weather.

3. Rosa is in her bedroom, but she *(sleep, not)* _____. She *(clean)*
   _____.

4. My roommates *(relax)* _____ in front of the TV this evening.
   They *(study, not)* _____.

5. I *(write)* _____ the correct answers. I *(make, not)*
   _____ mistakes.

Part B   *Directions:* Complete the sentences. Use the simple present or the present progressive form of the verbs in parentheses.

1. Rita sometimes *(wear)* _____ jeans to school, but today she *(wear)*
   _____ a dress.

2. Oh no! A bee *(fly)* _____ around my head. I *(be)*
   _____ afraid of bees!

3. Samir and Fatima *(be)* _____ at the zoo today. Right now, they
   (watch) _____ a tiger. The tiger *(eat)* _____
   meat. Tigers *(eat)* _____ meat every day.

4. I *(need)* _____ a dictionary right now. I *(understand, not)*
   _____ this word.

Part C   *Directions:* Circle the correct completions.

1. A: _____ your roommates eating lunch now?

   a. Is   b. Are   c. Do

   B: No, they _____.

   a. isn't   b. aren't   c. don't

2. A: Is Rob _____ many photos today?

   a. take   b. takes   c. taking

   B: Yes, he _____.

   a. is   b. does   c. taking

3. A: Does Sunita _____ to go home now?

   a. want   b. wants   c. wanting

   B: No, _____.

   a. she's not   b. she isn't   c. she doesn't

4. A: _____ a story right now?

   a. Do you read   b. Are reading   c. Are you reading

   B: Yes, I _____.

   a. do   b. am   c. are

5. A: Why _____ speaking Spanish?

   a. Jim and Luisa are   b. do Jim and Luisa   c. are Jim and Luisa

   B: Because Luisa's mother is here. She doesn't understand English.

6. A: What _____ for dinner tonight?

   a. Jun cooking   b. is Jun cooking   c. does Jun cook

   B: Vegetables and rice.

Part D   *Directions:* Correct the errors.

1. Right now Alex doing his homework. He's studing grammar.

2. Do you think about grammar right now?

3. Pedro no siting in his seat. Is he in the hallway?

4. I look at the sky right now. I'm seeing black clouds.

5. Tina is kissing her baby now. The baby is smileing.

Talking About the Present

Using *It* to Talk About Time   (Chart 5-1)

Directions: Make questions. Begin each question with ***What.***

Example: A: _____*What month is it?*_____

B: It's October.

1. A: _____

   B: It's Friday.

2. A: _____

   B: It's eleven o'clock.

3. A: _____

   B: Two thousand and _____.

4. A: _____

   B: It's 8:00 A.M.

5. A: _____

   B: May.

6. A: _____

   B: October 6th, 2 _____.

7. A: _____

   B: I'm not sure. I think it's around two-fifteen.

8. A: _____

   B: The 24th of February.

9. A: _____

   B: Wednesday.

10. A: _____

    B: It's December 15th.

Directions: Write a **true** answer for each question. Begin each answer with **It's**.

1. What time is it? _____

2. What's the date today? _____

3. What day is it? _____

4. What month is it? _____

5. What year is it? _____

Directions: Complete the sentences. Use *at, in, on, from,* or *to*.

Example: My grandfather was born _____*in*_____ 1940.

1. Chen's birthday is . . .
   a. _____ January.
   b. _____ Saturday this year.
   c. _____ January 12th.

2. I usually take the bus . . .
   a. _____ four o'clock.
   b. _____ Fridays.

3. My grandfather . . .
   a. gets up early _____ the morning.
   b. works _____ 10:00 A.M. _____ 6:00 P.M.
   c. usually stays home _____ the evening.
   d. rarely goes out _____ night.

Directions: Write a question and an answer about the weather in some American cities. Use the information given and the words from the box. Use each word once. Begin each question with ***What's*** or ***How's.*** Begin each answer with ***It's.*** More than one answer is possible. The first one is an example.

below freezing	clear	cold	✓ hot	stormy	warm
chilly	cloudy	cool	✓ humid	sunny	windy

Miami
94°F / 34°C
wet

1. A: _____ *What's the weather like / How's the weather in Miami?* _____
   B: _____ *It's hot and humid.* _____

Denver
50°F / 10°C
bright sunshine

2. A: _____
   B: _____

Honolulu
66°F / 19°C
clouds

3. A: _____
   B: _____

Seattle
35°F / 2°C
wind and rain

4. A: _____
   B: _____

Los Angeles
87°F / 31°C
no clouds

5. A: _____
   B: _____

Chicago
8°F / –13°C
strong winds

6. A: _____
   B: _____

Directions: Complete the sentences with **is** or **are**.

Example: There _____is_____ a beautiful park in this city.

SITUATION: *In the Park*

1. There _____ a lot of people in the park.

2. There _____ many trees in the park.

3. There _____ three birds in that tree.

4. There _____ a squirrel in the tree too.

5. There _____ a lake in the park.

6. There _____ some small boats on the lake.

7. There _____ several paths in the park.

8. There _____ runners on the paths every day.

9. There _____ a play area for children.

10. There _____ many children in the play area.

QUIZ 6 **There + Be: Yes/No Questions** (Chart 5-5)

Directions: Complete the questions with **Is there** or **Are there** and the words in *italics*. Then complete the short answers.

Example: a zoo A: _____Is there a zoo_____ in this city?

B: Yes, ___there is___. The zoo is wonderful!

SITUATION: *At the Zoo*

1. *any bears*   A: _____ in the zoo?

 B: Yes, _____.

2. *a cow*   A: _____ in the zoo?

 B: No, _____.

3. *a tiger*   A: _____ in the zoo?

 B: Yes, _____.

4. *any dogs*   A: _____ in the zoo?

 B: No, _____.

5. *a restaurant*   A: _____ at the zoo?

 B: Yes, _____, but the food is terrible!

A. *Directions:* Make a question for each answer. Use *How many* and the given words.

Example: letters / in the English alphabet

A: _____How many letters are there in the English alphabet?_____

B: There are 26 letters in the English alphabet.

SITUATION: *World Facts*

1. states / in Mexico

   A: _____?

   B: There are 31 states in Mexico.

2. national holidays / in Japan

   A: _____?

   B: There are 15 national holidays in Japan.

3. professional baseball teams / in the USA

   A: _____?

   B: There are 20 professional baseball teams in the USA.

4. minutes / in a day

   A: _____?

   B: There are 1,440 minutes in a day.

5. national languages / in Switzerland

   A: _____?

   B: There are 4 national languages in Switzerland.

B. *Directions:* Write a true answer for each question. Use *There is* or *There are*.

Example: How many days are there in September?

_____*There are 30 days in September.*_____

1. How many people are there in this room?

   _____

2. How many hours are there in a day?

   _____

3. How many questions are there on this quiz?

   _____

4. How many days are there in a week?

   _____

5. How many children are there in your family?

   _____

A. *Directions:* Complete the sentences with *in, on,* or *at*. The first one is an example.

SITUATION: *Where People Live*

1. Antonio lives ___in___ Chicago. He lives _____ 3631 Grand Avenue.

2. Martha lives _____ Morgan Street _____ New York City. She lives _____ 262 Morgan Street.

3. Antonio and Martha live _____ the United States.

B. *Directions:* Complete the sentences with prepositions from the box. Use each preposition once. The first one is an example.

around	in back of	in the back of
far away from	in front of	✓ in the front of

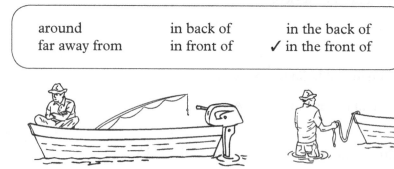

1. The man is sitting _in the front of_ the boat.

2. The man is standing _____ the boat.

3. The man is sitting _____ the boat.

4. The man is standing _____ the boat.

5. The hand is _____ the fishing pole.
The fish isn't near the fishing pole.
It is _____ the fishing pole.

Directions: Change the sentences to *would like*.

Example: We want to go to a restaurant.

_____We would like / We'd like to go_____ to a restaurant.

SITUATION: *Going Out for Dinner*

1. We want Thai food.

_____ Thai food.

2. A: Do you want to come with us?

_____ with us?

   B: Yes, I want to go with you.
   Yes, _____ with you.

3. Liz wants to have some vegetables.

_____ some vegetables.

4. She wants rice with her vegetables.

_____ rice with her vegetables.

5. Tarek and Sam want to eat *Pad Thai*.

_____ *Pad Thai*.

6. They want hot, spicy food.

_____ hot, spicy food.

7. A: Does Ruth want a glass of Thai iced tea?

_____ a glass of Thai iced tea?

   B: Yes, she does.
   Yes, _____.

8. We want to pay for our dinner now.

_____ for our dinner now.

Directions: Rewrite the conversations. Make the meaning of the second sentence similar to the meaning of the first sentence. Use the correct form of **would like** or **like**. Some sentences are negative.

Examples: I want some chocolate. I _____would like_____ some chocolate.

I enjoy dark chocolate. I _____like_____ dark chocolate.

SITUATION: *I'm Hungry*

1. A: I enjoy fruit.

B: Do you want a banana?

A: No, I don't enjoy them.

   I want some strawberries.

A: I _____ fruit.

B: _____ a banana?

A: I _____ bananas.

   I _____ some
   strawberries.

SITUATION: *Free Time Activities*

2. A: Do you enjoy sports?

B: Yes, I do. I enjoy them.

A: Do want to play tennis?

B: I don't enjoy tennis.

   I enjoy swimming.

   Do you want to go swimming?

A: Sure!

A: _____ sports?

B: Yes, I do. I _____ sports.

A: _____ to play tennis?

B: I _____ tennis.

B: I _____ swimming.

B: _____ to go swimming?

B: Sure!

Directions: Complete the sentences with the words in parentheses. Use the simple present or the present progressive. Use an infinitive where necessary. The first one is an example.

Sam (*sit*) _____is sitting_____ in math class now. His classmates

(*do*) _____ an exercise. Sam (*look*) _____
   1   2

at the problems in his book. He (*understand*) _____
                                                3

the problems, but he (*write, not*) _____ the answers
                                        4

right now. He (*think*) _____ about soccer. He (*think*)
                            5   6

_____ that soccer is fun and exciting. Sam (*want, not*)
                                                              7

_____ (*stop*) _____ daydreaming, but he (*need*)
               8   9

_____ (*finish*) _____ the exercise.
                  10

Directions: Choose the correct completions. The first one is an example.

1. My friends live _____ Park Avenue.

    a. in   (b.) on   c. at

2. Does Tony have English class _____ the evening?

    a. in   b. on   c. at

3. A: What _____ today?

       a. is the date   b. the date is   c. the date

    B: _____ the 19th of May.

       a. It   b. Is   c. It's

4. There _____ in a day.

    a. is twenty-four hour   b. is twenty-four hours   c. are twenty-four hours

5. Bus drivers sit _____ the bus.

    a. in front of   b. in the front of   c. in front

6. A: _____ a glass of orange juice now?

       a. Are you like   b. Would you like   c. Do you like

    B: No, thank you.

7. How many _____ in your backpack?

    a. book is there   b. books there are   c. books are there

8. _____ any dictionaries in the library?

    a. Is there   b. Are there   c. There

9. A: What _____ in your hometown in May?

       a. the weather like   b. the weather is   c. is the weather like

    B: _____ mild and rainy.

       a. Is   b. It's   c. It likes

Directions: Correct the mistakes.

Example: We'd like_∧eat Chinese food tonight.

       to

1. There's six eggs in the refrigerator.

2. Juanita woulds like a glass of water.

3. What time it is?

4. Zahra takes the bus to school. She usually sits in front of the bus.

5. Bobby is sleepy. He would likes to go to bed now.

6. Alexa's birthday is in August 19th.

7. How many big cities there are in China?

8. My parents live in Spring Street.

9. The bank isn't open at Sundays.

10. How's the weather like in Seattle?

CHAPTER 5–TEST 1

Part A   *Directions:* Circle the correct completions.

1. A: What time _____?
   - a. is
   - b. it is
   - c. is it

   B: _____ eleven.
   - a. Is
   - b. It's
   - c. It

2. I eat lunch _____ noon.
   - a. at
   - b. in
   - c. on

3. We don't have class _____ Friday.
   - a. at
   - b. in
   - c. on

4. A: _____ in Miami today?
   - a. How's the weather
   - b. How the weather
   - c. What's the weather

   B: _____ cloudy and warm.
   - a. It
   - b. It's
   - c. Is

5. A: What month _____?
   - a. is
   - b. it is
   - c. is it

   B: _____.
   - a. October
   - b. Tuesday
   - c. Two thousand

6. A: When do you study?

   B: I usually study _____ 9 to 11P.M.
   - a. at
   - b. in
   - c. from

7. Ashray has class _____ the afternoon.
   - a. in
   - b. at
   - c. on

Part B   *Directions:* Complete the sentences with the correct form of ***there*** + ***be***. Use the simple present tense.

1. _____ a public swimming pool near my house.

2. A: _____ any oranges in the refrigerator?

   B: Yes, _____.

3. A: How many computers _____ in the library?

   B: _____ twelve computers in the library.

Directions: Circle the correct completions.

1. My grandparents live (*at, in, on*) Montreal, Canada.

2. I live (*at, in, on*) Broad Street, not Brown Street.

3. Otto is wearing a cap (*at, in, on*) his head.

4. My notebook is on the table and my pen is beside my notebook. This means that my pen is (*far away from, next to, inside*) my notebook.

5. We're finishing Chapter 5. It's (*above, between, below*) Chapter 4 and Chapter 6.

Part D *Directions:* Make the meaning of the second sentence similar to the meaning of the first sentence. Use the correct form of ***would like*** or ***like***. Some sentences are negative.

1. Tai wants eggs for breakfast.

   Tai _____ eggs for breakfast.

2. Anna enjoys her job very much.

   Anna _____ her job very much.

3. A: Do you want some rice?

   A: _____ some rice?

   B: No, thanks. I don't enjoy rice.

   B: No, thanks. I _____ rice.

4. Do you enjoy music?

   _____ music?

Part E *Directions:* Correct the mistakes.

1. What the weather like in Athens?

2. Tomas woulds like a steak for dinner tonight.

3. How many countries there are in North America?

4. Please sit in middle of the boat.

5. We live on 358 Norland Street.

CHAPTER 5—TEST 2

Part A   *Directions:* Circle the correct completions.

1. A: What month _____?

   a. it is   b. is it   c. is

   B: _____ June.

   a. It's   b. It   c. Is

2. A: What _____ today?

   a. is it the date   b. the date is   c. is the date

   B: _____.

   a. Tuesday   b. The 23rd of April   c. Nine-fifteen

3. My son was born _____ 2003.

   a. in   b. on   c. at

4. The cafeteria is open for breakfast from 7:00 _____ 9:00.

   a. at   b. to   c. in

5. A: What _____ in Los Angeles in the summer?

   a. is the weather like   b. the weather is   c. the weather like

   B: _____ warm and sunny every day.

   a. It likes   b. Is   c. It's

6. My birthday is _____ December 15th.

   a. on   b. at   c. in

7. _____ the weather in Seattle in the summer?

   a. What's   b. What's like   c. How's

Part B   *Directions:* Complete the sentences with the correct form of ***there*** + ***be***. Use the simple present tense.

1. Look! _____ a big green turtle in the water.

2. A: Let's have a picnic. _____ any cheese in the refrigerator?

   B: No, _____.

3. A: How many pictures _____ in the art museum?

   B: _____ hundreds of pictures in the art museum.

Part C *Directions:* Circle the correct completions.

1. Maria doesn't live (*at, in, on*) Market Street. She lives (*at, in, on*) 2402 Seventh Avenue.

   She lives (*at, in, on*) Redwood City, California.

2. I want to cook the food in this pot now. I need to put the pot (*at, above, on top of*) the stove.

3. Toshi's desk is in the front row. My desk is in the back row. This means that my desk is (*behind, below, between*) Toshi's desk.

Part D *Directions:* Make the meaning of the second sentence similar to the meaning of the first sentence. Use the correct form of **would like** or **like.** Some sentences are negative.

1. Ken and Toshiko want to visit Tokyo.   Ken and Toshiko _____ to visit Tokyo.

2. Laura doesn't enjoy working with animals.   Laura _____ working with animals.

3. What time do you want to eat dinner?   What time _____ to eat dinner?

4. A: Do you want a cup of coffee?   A: _____ a cup of coffee?

   B: Yes, please. I enjoy coffee.   B: Yes, please. I _____ coffee.

Part E *Directions:* Correct the mistakes.

1. How the weather is in Montreal?

2. Marcos would likes an ice cream cone.

3. How many days is there in June?

4. There's several good movies on TV tonight.

5. I'm like to watch TV now. How about you?

CHAPTER 6 Nouns and Pronouns

QUIZ 1 **Nouns** (Chart 6-1)

Directions: Check (√) the words that are nouns. The first one is an example.

1. __√__ French   4. _____ eat   7. _____ hungry   10. _____ rich

2. _____ math   5. _____ friends   8. _____ cats   11. _____ Moscow

3. _____ happy   6. _____ hotel   9. _____ lazy   12. _____ write

QUIZ 2 **Nouns as Objects** (Chart 6-1)

Directions: Check (√) the sentences that have objects. Then underline the objects. The first one is an example.

SITUATION: *Using My Cell Phone*

1. __√__ I have a <u>cell phone</u>.

2. _____ My cell phone is red.

3. _____ I use my cell phone every day.

4. _____ Sometimes I call my friends.

5. _____ I am texting right now.

6. _____ I send many text messages every day.

7. _____ Text messages are easy to send.

8. _____ I don't need to spell carefully.

9. _____ Texting in English is fun.

10. _____ My cell phone takes pictures too.

11. _____ I really like my cell phone.

Directions: Underline the prepositions. Circle the object of each preposition.

Example: I do my laundry <u>on</u> (Fridays.)

SITUATION: *My Brother's Apartment*

1. a. My brother lives in an apartment.

   b. His apartment is on the top floor.

   c. He can see across the city.

SITUATION: *Music Class*

2. a. Chang plays the violin at school.

   b. He sits between Yun and Lian.

   c. They often talk during class.

SITUATION: *A Good Book*

3. a. I am reading a story about the future.

   b. People travel by spaceship.

   c. There are people from Mars.

   d. There is a man with three eyes.

Directions: Describe the grammatical structure of the sentences as shown in the example.

Example: Olga works at a store.

Olga	works	(none)	at	a store
subject	verb	object of verb	preposition	object of prep.

1. The boys play games in the park.

subject	verb	object of verb	preposition	object of prep.

2. Ben and Lucia have a motorcycle.

subject	verb	object of verb	preposition	object of prep.

3. Alejandro speaks English and Spanish.

subject	verb	object of verb	preposition	object of prep.

4. The teacher is drawing a picture on the board.

subject	verb	object of verb	preposition	object of prep.

5. The students are talking about their plans.

subject	verb	object of verb	preposition	object of prep.

Adjectives with Nouns (Chart 6-3)

Directions: <u>Underline</u> the adjectives and circle the nouns. Draw an arrow from each adjective to the noun it describes.

Example: My (brother) likes <u>fast</u> (cars)

1. I sometimes put fresh flowers on my desk.
2. Mia needs a strong backpack for her heavy books.
3. My lazy roommate never changes his dirty socks.
4. Do your friends like Vietnamese food?
5. She'd like a big cup of hot coffee with sugar.
6. Do you want to read an interesting story about a famous woman?
7. Students often ask difficult questions.
8. Evie likes to wear black jeans.
9. A famous actress with beautiful hair stars in the movie.
10. Do you have exciting plans for your vacation?

QUIZ 6 **Subject and Object Pronouns** (Chart 6-4)

Directions: Complete the sentences with the correct object pronouns.

Example: **Elise** is a student. The teacher helps _____*her*_____ a lot.

1. **I** am a student. My teacher helps _____.
2. **You** are a student. Your teacher helps _____.
3. **Jana and Will** are students. The teacher helps _____.
4. **Mrs. Dann** is a teacher. The students like _____.
5. **Mr. Yang** is a teacher. The students like _____.
6. **It** is a grammar book. The students read _____.
7. **We** are students. The teachers teach _____.
8. **You** are teachers. The students like _____.
9. **The teachers** are nice. We like _____.
10. **English** is fun. We like _____.

Directions: Complete the sentences with the correct pronouns.

Example: A: Where is Robin?

  B: _____*He*_____ is in the kitchen. _____*He*_____ is cooking dinner.

1. A: Do you know Mr. and Mrs. Martinez?

  B: Yes, _____ do. I know _____ very well.

2. A: Does Nadia have a new laptop computer?

  B: Yes, _____ does. _____ uses _____ to surf the Internet.

3. A: Where are you going?

  B: My brother and I need to go home now. Our mother wants _____ to help her.

4. A: What's wrong? You look sad.

  B: I miss Anna. I call _____ every Sunday. _____ often talk for hours.

5. A: I'm going downtown. Would you like to come with _____?

  B: Yes, thanks. _____ would enjoy that very much.

Directions: Complete the list with the plural form of the nouns. The first one is an example.

SINGULAR	PLURAL
1. class	*classes*
2. thief	_____
3. tax	_____
4. zoo	_____
5. knife	_____
6. classmate	_____
7. party	_____
8. sandwich	_____
9. cowboy	_____
10. college	_____
11. tomato	_____

QUIZ 9 **Nouns: Regular and Irregular Plurals** (Charts 6-5 and 6-6)

Directions: Complete the sentences with the plural form of the words in *italics*. The first one is an example.

1. *package* I have two _____*packages*_____ of cookies. Would you like one?

2. *foot* My shoes are uncomfortable. My _____ hurt!

3. *fish* Dr. Lee has ten _____ in his aquarium. They are beautiful!

4. *city* China has many _____ with over a million people.

5. *man* My car has a problem. Two _____ are trying to fix it.

6. *mouse* Oh no! There are _____ in our kitchen.

7. *tooth* Our baby is eight months old. She has four _____ now.

8. *leaf* In autumn, the _____ change color and fall off the trees.

9. *sheep* My uncle in Canada has eighty _____ on his farm.

10. *woman* How many _____ are there in your class?

11. *child* The _____ are playing with their toys.

Directions: Circle the correct completions. The first one is an example.

1. I want to call my sister. I need to talk to _____.

   a. she   (b.) her   c. him

2. Jason has a cell phone. He always carries _____ in his pocket.

   a. it   b. him   c. them

3. Katya likes to read. _____ spends a lot of time at the library.

   a. Her   b. Us   c. She

4. I want to make sauce for the pasta. Are there any _____ in the refrigerator?

   a. tomato   b. tomatos   c. tomatoes

5. Joao and I are going to a movie tonight. Would you like to go with _____?

   a. it   b. us   c. them

6. Dina and _____ sometimes study together in the afternoon.

   a. me   b. I   c. us

7. Ms. Hopfe is kind. She often helps Niko and _____.

   a. me   b. I   c. we

8. My kids love swimming. _____ take swimming lessons every summer.

   a. They   b. Them   c. We

9. Those trees have red _____ in the autumn.

   a. leafs   b. leafes   c. leaves

10. I like this city. The _____ friendly here.

    a. people is   b. people are   c. peoples is

11. Pedro likes Anna. He thinks that she has _____.

    a. eyes beautifuls   b. beautiful eyes   c. beautifuls eyes

Possessive Adjectives and Possessive Pronouns (Chart 6-7)

Directions: Write the possessive forms to complete the chart.

OBJECT PRONOUNS	POSSESSIVE ADJECTIVES	POSSESSIVE PRONOUNS
1. This book belongs to **me**.	This is _____ book.	This book is _____.
2. That pen belongs to **you**.	That is _____ pen.	That pen is ___*yours*___.
3. This desk belongs to **her**.	This is _____ desk.	This desk is _____.
4. That phone belongs to **him**.	That is ___*his*___ phone.	That phone is _____.
5. This car belongs to **us**.	This is _____ car.	This car is _____.
6. That car belongs to **them**.	That is _____ car.	That car is _____.

Possessive Adjectives and Possessive Pronouns (Chart 6-7)

Directions: Choose the correct completions. The first one is an example.

1. A: (*Your,* Yours) sandwich looks good. What's in it?

   B: Cheese and tomatoes. What's in (*your, yours*)?

   A: (*My, Mine*) has beef and tomatoes in it. Do you want to try it? I'll give you half
   of (*my, mine*) sandwich if you give me half of (*your, yours*).

   B: No, thanks.

2. A: Is this Maria's dictionary?

   B: I'm not sure. It might be (*her, hers*). Is (*her, hers*) name in it?

   A: No, it isn't. I'll ask Spiro. Maybe this dictionary is (*him, his*).

3. A: Eric and Jeanne moved to a new apartment.

   B: Really? Where is (*their, theirs*) new apartment? Is it close to (*your, yours*)?

   A: Yes, it is. (*Our, Ours*) apartment is on Second Avenue, and they live on Third
   Avenue.

Possessive Nouns (Chart 6-8)

Directions: Complete the sentences. Use the possessive form of the words in *italics*.

Example: sister My _____*sister's*_____ name is Morena.

1. *Andrea*   _____ parents live in Venezuela.

2. *brothers*   My _____ names are Max and Leo.

3. *mother*   My Aunt Lily is my _____ sister.

4. *parents*   My _____ house is near the ocean.

5. *boy*   Where is that _____ mother?

6. *Sergei*   Do you know _____ telephone number?

7. *friends*   I have all of my _____ numbers on my contacts list.

8. *teacher*   My English _____ name is Ms. Han.

9. *doctor*   Where is your _____ office?

10. *Clay*   _____ favorite sport is volleyball.

Apostrophes with Possessives and *Is* (Chapter 1 and Chart 6-8)

Directions: Add apostrophes where necessary. If a sentence does not need an apostrophe, write **NC** for **no change**.

Examples: My fathers first name is Arturo. _*father's*_

My parents live in Chicago. _*NC*_

SITUATION: *Family and Friends*

1. a. One of my aunts has two daughters. _____

   b. My aunts name is Anna. _____

   c. My cousins names are Susan and Elizabeth. _____

2. a. My parents are visiting my grandparents. _____

   b. My grandparents house is in the country. _____

   c. My mothers helping my grandmother. _____

3. a. One of my classmates shares an apartment with me. _____

   b. My roommates name is Matt. _____

   c. My roommates studying engineering. _____

   d. Matt and I have some friends in the dormitory. Our friends rooms are

      small. _____

A. *Directions:* Choose the correct completions. The first one is an example.

1. Whose sunglasses _____*are*_____ _____*these*_____?
   is, are   this, these

2. Whose umbrella _____ _____?
   is, are   that, those

3. Whose newspaper _____ _____?
   is, are   this, these

4. Whose shoes _____ _____?
   is, are   this, these

5. Whose coins _____ _____?
   is, are   that, those

6. Whose homework _____ _____?
   is, are   this, these

B. *Directions:* Complete the sentences with *Whose* or *Who's*. The first one is an example.

1. _____*Who's*_____ your teacher?

2. _____ picture is this?

3. _____ coming to the party?

4. _____ is this?

5. _____ turn is it?

6. _____ next?

Possessives: Irregular Plural Nouns (Charts 6-8 and 6-10)

Directions: Complete each sentence with the possessive form of the nouns in *italics*.

Example: girls This store sells _____ *girls'* _____ clothing.

1. *people*   Can you find _____ email addresses on the Internet?

2. *women*   My mom likes to watch _____ sports.

3. *students* The teacher is going to check the _____ quizzes soon.

4. *wife*   Evan doesn't like his _____ family.

5. *men*   That big building is a _____ dormitory.

6. *woman*   Do you know that _____ husband?

7. *friends*   I'm interested in my _____ lives.

8. *person*   You can sometimes find a _____ home address on the Internet.

9. *man*   Is Kelly a _____ name?

10. *children* There are some very good _____ programs on TV.

Chapter Review

Directions: Correct the mistakes.

Example: Mr. Reichart lives in ~~mine~~ neighborhood.
                                    my

1. Who's boots are these?

2. Rasheed a new phone has.

3. Do you like to go to partys?

4. How many man are there in your class?

5. My roommate and me have a big TV in our room.

6. My aunt has two little childs.

7. Whose going to study for the test with you?

8. Those aren't Marys glasses. Hers are in her purse.

9. There are two language in Canada. People speaks English and French.

CHAPTER 6–TEST 1

Part A   *Directions:* Describe the grammatical structure of the sentences.

1. Karina makes breakfast for her children.

subject	verb	object of verb	preposition	object of prep.

2. Max and Mary live in the country.

subject	verb	object of verb	preposition	object of prep.

3. I like sunny weather.

subject	verb	object of verb	preposition	object of prep.

4. The wind is blowing.

subject	verb	object of verb	preposition	object of prep.

Part B   *Directions:* Circle the correct completions.

1. I know Mrs. Kwan. (*She, Her, He*) works in my office.
2. My grandfather is sick. I want to visit (*he, him, her*).
3. Those books aren't Lucia's. They are (*I, my, mine*).
4. Do you want this sandwich? (*It's, They're, You're*) delicious.
5. Tina hates vegetables. She never eats (*it, them, her*).

Part C   *Directions:* Complete the sentences with the plural form of a noun from the box. Use each noun once.

> child   city   dish   foot   key   wife

1. Toronto and Quebec are _____ in Canada.
2. Chris has big _____, so he needs big shoes.
3. Elsa loves _____. She wants to have a big family.
4. Both of my brothers are married. They have _____.
5. This door has two locks, so you need two _____ to open it.
6. The dinner is ready. Let's put the _____ and silverware on the table.

Part D   *Directions:* Complete the sentences with the possessive form of the words in *italics*.

1. *you* This pen is _____.

   Tony That pen is _____.

   You _____ pen has black ink.

   he _____ pen has blue ink.

2. *Sarah* These books are _____.

   she _____ are on the desk.

   the men Those are _____.

   they They need _____ books for class.

3. *doctor* I work at a _____ office.

   we Sunday is _____ day off.

Part E   *Directions:* Complete the sentences with **Whose** or **Who's**.

1. _____ at the door?

2. _____ camera is that?

3. _____ is this?

4. _____ bringing food to the picnic?

5. _____ hungry? Dinner is ready!

Part F   *Directions:* Correct the mistakes.

1. My friend is a dancer good.

2. Jorge and me play tennis every Saturday.

3. That dictionary doesn't belong to me. Mine dictionary is red.

4. There are two zooes in this city.

5. Ladys drink tea at the Empress Hotel.

6. Are these yours keys?

7. Womens' clothing is on the third floor.

8. My wifes sister works in a hospital.

9. Two of my classmate's are planning a party.

10. Whose coming to the movie with us?

CHAPTER 6–TEST 2

Part A *Directions:* Describe the grammatical structure of the sentences.

1. We visit our grandparents on holidays.

subject	verb	object of verb	preposition	object of prep.

2. My cousins live in France.

subject	verb	object of verb	preposition	object of prep.

3. The phone is ringing.

subject	verb	object of verb	preposition	object of prep.

4. Gil enjoys the fresh air in the mountains.

subject	verb	object of verb	preposition	object of prep.

Part B *Directions:* Circle the correct completions.

1. Mr. Anderson is a police officer. Do you know (*her, him, he*)?

2. Do you want to use (*me, my, mine*) computer?

3. June is looking for her keys. Do you see (*they, them, it*)?

4. Ada is very nice. Carol and (*I, me, my*) often go to her house.

5. Pedro and Juan are playing cards. "Crazy Eights" is (*they, them, their*) favorite game.

Part C *Directions:* Complete the sentences with the plural form of a noun from the box. Use each noun once.

> day   dictionary   glass   knife   tomato   tooth

1. Jerry is in the bathroom. He's brushing his _____.

2. People usually use _____ to cut meat.

3. Many students in my English class use electronic _____ to look up new words.

4. The month of December has thirty-one _____.

5. I'm very hot and thirsty. I'd like two _____ of water.

6. My father grows delicious _____ in his vegetable garden.

Part D *Directions:* Complete the sentences with the possessive form of the words in *italics*.

1. *I*   This coffee is _____.

   you   That coffee is _____.

   I   _____ coffee has milk in it.

   you   _____ coffee has sugar in it.

2. *Jake*   Paulo is _____ roommate.

   they   _____ room is always neat and clean.

   we   _____ room is usually messy.

3. *children* These are my _____ drawings.

   Maya   That one is _____.

   she   It has _____ name on it.

Part E *Directions:* Complete the sentences with **Whose** or **Who's**.

1. _____ phone is ringing?

2. _____ grammar book is that?

3. _____ living in that house now?

4. _____ ready to go home?

5. _____ keys are on the table?

Part F *Directions:* Correct the mistakes.

1. My grandmother in a small house lives.

2. Would you like to watch TV with my roommate and I?

3. My aunts are nice womans.

4. My mothers' brothers live in Venezuela.

5. Whose watch are this?

6. That blue car isn't our.

7. The teacher's are having a meeting next Monday.

8. Some students left theirs books in the classroom.

9. Whose finished with the test?

10. There are seven peoples in my family.

CHAPTER 7 Count and Noncount Nouns

Nouns: Count and Noncount (Chart 7-1)

Directions: Look at the noun in *italics*. Decide if it is count or noncount. Choose the correct answer. The first one is an example.

1.	My brother sends a lot of text *messages*.	(count)	noncount
2.	Do you like rock *music*?	count	noncount
3.	I want to buy some *bananas*.	count	noncount
4.	Charles drinks a lot of *tea*.	count	noncount
5.	We need to learn a lot of new *vocabulary*.	count	noncount
6.	Mariah gets a lot of *mail*.	count	noncount
7.	I'd like a *cup* of coffee, please.	count	noncount
8.	I have a lot of *homework* every day.	count	noncount
9.	Josh watches a lot of *movies*.	count	noncount
10.	Mr. Bell has a lot of *work* to do.	count	noncount
11.	Many women wear *jewelry*.	count	noncount

Nouns: Count and Noncount (Chart 7-1)

Directions: Complete the chart with words from the list. Use each word once. Use the plural form of the count nouns. The first one is an example.

✓assignment	fact	jewelry	money	song	word
car	fruit	mail	sofa	weather	

	NONCOUNT NOUNS	COUNT NOUNS
1.	homework	*assignments*
2.	_____	coins
3.	furniture	_____
4.	_____	apples
5.	music	_____
6.	_____	rings
7.	_____	storms
8.	information	_____
9.	_____	postcards
10.	traffic	_____
11.	vocabulary	_____

Directions: Complete the sentences with the words in *italics*. Use the plural form of the count nouns.

Example: *jewelry*   The queen has some beautiful _____ jewelry _____ .

   earring   She has some _____ earrings _____ with blue diamonds.

SITUATION: *Studying*

1. *homework*   He has some _____ to finish tonight.

2. *coffee*   He's sleepy. He needs some strong _____ .

SITUATION: *Winter Weather*

3. *weather*   We're having some stormy _____ this winter.

4. *cloud*   I see some dark _____ in the sky now.

SITUATION: *Cooking*

5. *tomato*   I need some ripe _____ and some

   meat   _____ for the spaghetti sauce.

SITUATION: *Taking the Bus*

6. *woman*   Some _____ are standing at the bus stop.

7. *coin*   We need some _____ to pay the bus driver.

8. *money*   I have some _____ in my pocket.

SITUATION: *Healthy Food*

9. *fruit*   It's a good idea to eat some _____ every day.

Directions: Write *a* or *an*. The first one is an example.

1. _an_ office

2. _____ house

3. _____ expensive house

4. _____ apartment

5. _____ noisy apartment

6. _____ hour

7. _____ hungry child

8. _____ honor student

9. _____ university

10. _____ umbrella

11. _____ yellow umbrella

Directions: Complete the sentences with *a, an,* or *some.* Then decide if the noun in *italics* is singular count, plural count, or noncount. Circle the correct answer. The first one is an example.

SITUATION: *About Me*

1. I'd like . . .

   _____some_____ *cheese.*   singular count   plural count   (noncount)

   _____ *apple.*   singular count   plural count   noncount

   _____ *french fries.*   singular count   plural count   noncount

   _____ *water.*   singular count   plural count   noncount

2. I have . . .

   _____ *information* for you.   singular count   plural count   noncount

   _____ *questions* for you.   singular count   plural count   noncount

   _____ *umbrella* for you.   singular count   plural count   noncount

3. I want to buy . . .

   _____ new *furniture.*   singular count   plural count   noncount

   _____ new *chairs.*   singular count   plural count   noncount

   _____ new *table.*   singular count   plural count   noncount

   _____ used *car.*   singular count   plural count   noncount

Directions: Complete the sentences with *a, an,* or *some.* The first one is an example.

1. I'm using ____some____ vegetables to make soup. I need _____ onion and

   _____ carrots.

2. Mr. Klassen has _____ information about what to do in _____

   emergency at work.

3. I'm living in _____ apartment. I want to buy _____ furniture.

   I need _____ new table and _____ chairs.

4. Would you like _____ cup of coffee, or _____ tea?

SITUATION: *Shopping with Tomas and Paula*

A. Directions: Complete Tomas' shopping list with words from the list. Use each word once. The first one is an example.

> bottle   bunch   head   ✓loaf   piece   tube

Tomas needs to buy . . .

1. a _____*loaf*_____ of bread.
2. a _____ of cheese.
3. a _____ of olive oil.

4. a _____ of toothpaste.
5. a _____ of lettuce.
6. a _____ of bananas.

B. Directions: Complete Paula's shopping list with words from the list. Use each word once. The first one is an example.

> candy   ✓corn   pickles   rice   soap   water

Paula needs to buy. . .

1. a can of _____*corn*_____.
2. a jar of _____.
3. a bottle of _____.

4. a box of _____.
5. a bag of _____.
6. a bar of _____.

Directions: Complete the sentences. Use *a piece of*, *a cup of*, *a glass of*, or *a bowl of*. More than one answer may be correct. The first one is an example.

SITUATION: *Linda's Daily Menu*

Linda usually eats healthy food. She always eats _____*a bowl of*_____ cereal

for breakfast. She usually drinks _____ coffee before class. For a
                                                    1

snack she likes to have _____ cheese or _____
                                          2   3

orange juice. For lunch she usually eats _____ chicken and
                                                  4

_____ rice, but sometimes she has _____ soup and
        5   6

_____ bread. For dinner, Linda likes to have _____
        7   8

meat and _____ salad. Linda usually has _____
                  9   10

milk before she goes to bed.

QUIZ 9 *Much* and *Many* (Chart 7-5)

Directions: Complete the sentences with *many* or *much*.

Example: Yoko doesn't eat _____ much _____ chicken.

1. Ali doesn't drink _____ milk.

2. Poor Harry! He doesn't have _____ friends.

3. Sophia doesn't wear _____ jewelry.

4. I don't have _____ rings.

5. Laura has a new baby, so she doesn't get _____ sleep.

6. My son's soccer team plays _____ games.

7. How _____ children does your aunt have?

8. How _____ rice do you want in your bowl?

9. How _____ sugar do you put in your tea?

10. How _____ oranges do you need for the recipe?

QUIZ 10 *A Few* and *A Little* (Chart 7-5)

Directions: Complete the sentences with *a few* or *a little* and the nouns in *italics*.
Make the count nouns plural.

Examples: pencils   I need to buy _____ a few pencils _____ .

       salt   I usually put _____ a little salt _____ on my food.

1. *money*   Nan has _____ in the bank.

2. *coin*   Andy has _____ in his pocket.

3. *cheese*   I'd like _____ on my spaghetti.

4. *apple*   I usually put _____ in my fruit salad.

5. *work*   Jason has _____ to do this afternoon.

6. *assignment*   The students need to finish _____ this week.

7. *picture*   Ms. Jones has _____ of her family on her desk.

8. *music*   Let's turn on the radio and listen to _____ .

9. *friend*   I want to invite _____ to my party.

10. *city*   Only _____ in the US have a subway.

Directions: Circle the correct words for the noun in *italics*. More than one word may be correct. The first one is an example.

1. (a cup of)   a few   (some)   *coffee*
2. a   many   much   *traffic*
3. a   some   many   *table*
4. some   a little   a few   *sandwiches*
5. many   much   a few   *people*
6. an   many   a little   *information*
7. a few   a jar of   a loaf of   *pickles*
8. an   a little   a few   *animals*
9. some   a little   much   *help*
10. an   much   a little   *hour*
11. some   a little   a few   *advice*

Directions: Complete the sentences with *the*, *a*, or *an*.

Example: We have _____*an*_____ assignment to finish. _____*The*_____ assignment isn't difficult.

1. Carolina is wearing _____ sweater and _____ skirt today. _____ sweater is red and _____ skirt is black.

2. I have _____ sandwich and _____ apple in my backpack. _____ sandwich is for lunch. _____ apple is for a snack.

3. There's _____ art museum in my hometown. There's _____ restaurant in _____ museum. _____ restaurant has wonderful food. I like to order _____ cup of soup for lunch.

4. My sister has _____ new phone. It's very cool! _____ phone has _____ very good camera. _____ camera takes very clear pictures. My sister sends our parents _____ pictures she takes. I want _____ new phone, too!

Directions: Complete the conversations with *the, a,* or *an*.

Example: A: I'm looking for Professor Jones. Is she in class now?

B: No, she isn't. She's in _____the_____ library.

1. A: Mom, I'm hungry. I want _____ snack.

   B: You can go into _____ kitchen and look in _____ refrigerator
   for some fruit or cheese.

2. A: _____ weather is nice today, isn't it?

   B: Yes. _____ sun is shining, and there aren't any clouds in _____
   sky.

3. A: I need to write _____ note. Do you have _____ pen?

   B: Just a minute. I'll find one for you.

4. A: Do you need to use _____ car today?

   B: No, I don't. You can use it.

5. A: What do you want to do now?

   B: I have _____ idea. Let's go shopping. I want to buy some boots.

Directions: Complete the sentences with *the* or Ø (no article).

Example: I like __Ø__ cats.

1. _____ vegetables are good for you.

2. Anna, you need to eat _____ vegetables on your plate.

3. _____ water in this glass tastes awful.

4. _____ water is necessary for life.

5. I hate _____ traffic.

6. I'm driving to school now. _____ traffic is very heavy.

7. _____ nurses take care of sick people.

8. _____ nurses in Dr. Wu's office are very helpful.

9. Keiko is taking a math test. _____ problems on the test are difficult.

10. _____ math problems are not easy for me.

Some and Any (Chart 7-8)

Directions: Complete the conversations with **some** or **any**. If both are OK, use **some/ any**.

Example: A: Do you need ___some / any___ groceries?

      B: Yes, I need to buy ___some___ vegetables.

1. A: I want to write a note, but I need _____ paper. Do you have

      _____ paper?

   B: No, sorry. I don't have _____ paper.

2. A: Mom, I'm hungry. There's _____ cheese in the refrigerator, but there

      isn't _____ bread for sandwiches.

   B: You can have _____ cheese and crackers.

3. A: Nadia needs to study English now. She needs to learn _____ new

      vocabulary.

   B: Does Nadia need _____ help with her homework?

4. A: Linda wants to light the candles. Do you have _____ matches?

   B: I don't have _____ matches, but maybe Bob does.

Any vs. A/An (Charts 7-1, 7-2, and 7-8)

Directions: Complete the sentences. Use **a** or **an** with singular count nouns, and **any** with noncount nouns and plural count nouns.

Example: Tom doesn't want ___any___ fruit.

1. Luis doesn't want _____ apple.

2. Yoko is sad because there isn't _____ mail in her mailbox.

3. We don't have _____ classes on Saturdays.

4. What a nice day! There isn't _____ cloud in the sky.

5. I don't have _____ uncle named Matt. His name is Max.

6. It's Sunday, so there aren't _____ people in the office.

7. My grandmother doesn't have _____ cell phone.

8. I'm sorry. I don't have _____ information about the zoo.

9. They don't have _____ plans for the weekend.

10. Mr. Marcy doesn't have _____ time to meet with us today.

Directions: Choose the correct completions. The first one is an example.

1. Our history class lasts _____ hour.

   a. a   (b.) an   c. some

2. _____ university has many students and teachers.

   a. A   b. An   c. Some

3. I have _____ oranges in this bag.

   a. a   b. an   c. some

4. This street is always full of _____.

   a. a traffic   b. traffic   c. traffics

5. There's a _____ of lettuce in the refrigerator.

   a. glass   b. jar   c. head

6. Pieter doesn't eat _____ rice.

   a. much   b. many   c. a few

7. Do you take _____ notes in class?

   a. much   b. many   c. a little

8. Janey has _____ problems.

   a. much   b. a little   c. a few

9. My parents come from a small village. _____ is near Mexico City.

   a. A village   b. The village   c. Village

10. Everybody needs _____ to live.

    a. a water   b. the water   c. water

11. Look at _____! It's very bright tonight.

    a. a moon   b. the moon   c. moon

12. Erik doesn't want _____ fruit right now.

    a. a   b. any   c. some

13. We need _____ new dishes.

    a. a little   b. any   c. some

14. This book has _____ interesting information in it.

    a. a   b. an   c. some

15. Marco usually doesn't get _____ mail.

    a. a   b. any   c. some

16. Alicia has _____ aunt in London.

    a. a   b. an   c. any

CHAPTER 7–TEST 1

Part A *Directions:* Complete the sentences with the words in *italics*. Use the plural form of the count nouns.

1. *water* Roberto drinks a lot of _____.

2. *friend* Abdul has a lot of _____.

3. *assignment* Do you have a lot of _____ to do?

4. *work* We have a lot of _____ to finish.

5. *help* Barbara needs a lot of _____.

Part B *Directions:* Circle the correct completions.

1. Do you usually eat a ___ of cereal for breakfast?
   a. bottle   b. bowl   c. glass

2. My roommate and I have a small room, so we don't need ___.
   a. many furnitures   b. many furniture   c. much furniture

3. How ___ does your teacher speak?
   a. much languages   b. many languages   c. many language

4. I always put ___ on my eggs.
   a. a little salt   b. a little salts   c. a few salts

5. Would you like ___ on your ice cream?
   a. a little strawberries   b. a few strawberry   c. a few strawberries

6. Mrs. Park has ___ for us.
   a. some advice   b. some advices   c. any advice

7. There isn't ___ in the refrigerator.
   a. a cheese   b. some cheese   c. any cheese

8. I don't have ___ to do my homework in the evening.
   a. an time   b. much time   c. many times

9. A monkey can eat a ____ of bananas quickly.
   a. head   b. loaf   c. bunch

10. Do you need ___ money?
   a. a   b. any   c. many

Part C *Directions:* Complete the sentences with *a, an,* or *the*.

1. I have _____ coat and _____ umbrella in the closet. _____ coat is green and _____ umbrella is black.

2. A: Where's my notebook? Do you see it?
   B: Yes, I do. It's on _____ floor.

Part D *Directions:* Complete the sentences with *the* or *Ø* (no article).

1. Lemons are yellow, and _____ tomatoes are red.

2. _____ tomatoes at the farmer's market are fresh and delicious.

3. _____ computers in the library aren't working right now.

4. _____ computers are useful machines.

Part E *Directions:* Correct the mistakes.

1. Emily doesn't get many mails.

2. I need an advice.

3. There's a orange for you in the refrigerator.

4. Do you want to listen to some musics now?

5. How much chairs do you have in your room?

6. Kenji doesn't want some tea.

CHAPTER 7–TEST 2

Part A **Directions:** Complete the sentences with the words in *italics*. Use the plural form of the count nouns.

1. *question*   I have a lot of _____ to ask you.

2. *jewelry*   Ellen usually wears a lot of _____.

3. *child*   Does Sam want to have a lot of _____?

4. *information*   You have a lot of helpful _____ about traveling.

5. *weather*   Does New York have a lot of hot _____?

Part B **Directions:** Circle the correct completions.

1. When you go to the store, please buy a _____ of corn.

   a. bar   b. can   c. loaf

2. Winter is coming, so the trees don't have _____ on them now.

   a. much leaf   b. much leaves   c. many leaves

3. These problems are difficult, but I don't need _____ with them.

   a. much help   b. much helps   c. many helps

4. This city has _____ to visit.

   a. many interesting place   b. many interesting places   c. much interesting place

5. How _____ do you usually do in a day?

   a. many work   b. much work   c. many works

6. How _____ of paper do you need?

   a. many sheets   b. a sheet   c. much sheet

7. I usually put _____ on the dinner table.

   a. a little candles   b. a few candles   c. a few candle

8. We don't have _____ in the kitchen.

   a. any clean glass   b. any clean glasses   c. some clean glasses

9. There are _____ on the walls of my room.

   a. any beautiful pictures   b. many beautiful picture   c. some beautiful pictures

10. Celia has _____ mail to drop off at the post office.

    a. some   b. any   c. a

Part C *Directions:* Complete the sentences with *a, an,* or *the*.

1. Where's your sister? Is she in _____ kitchen?

2. A: What's _____ weather like outside right now?

   B: It's cool. _____ sun is behind some clouds.

3. I have _____ black jacket and _____ orange jacket.

Part D *Directions:* Complete the sentences with *the* or *Ø* (no article).

1. Does Selena like _____ music on this CD?

2. Willy likes to listen to _____ music when he studies.

3. _____ elephants are large animals.

4. _____ elephants in this zoo come from Africa.

Part E *Directions:* Correct the mistakes.

1. Pablo doesn't want some cheese on his hamburger.

2. We don't have much warm clothes.

3. I need a dictionary. I want to look up some word.

4. Greg is thirsty. He wants glass of water.

5. A: Are you wearing the watch? Do you know the correct time?

   B: It's 9:45.

6. I'd like a apple, please.

Expressing Past Time, Part 1

The Simple Past of *Be*   (Chart 8-1)

Directions: Complete the sentences. Change them to past time. Follow the example.

Example: The weather is nice today. The weather _____ *was nice yesterday, too.* _____

1. My brother is tired today.

   My brother _____.

2. I am busy today.

   I _____.

3. Max and Hans are at school today.

   Max and Hans _____.

4. A soccer game is on TV today.

   A soccer game _____.

5. Alice is in her office today.

   Alice _____.

6. My sister and I are in Chicago today.

   My sister and I _____.

7. You are at home today.

   You _____.

8. Fiona is sick today.

   Fiona _____.

9. Mr. and Mrs. Patten are on a trip today.

   Mr. and Mrs. Patten _____.

10. I am with my family today.

    I _____.

Directions: Complete the sentences with ***wasn't*** or ***weren't***.

Example: Katie is a serious student this year, but she _____*wasn't*_____ a serious student last year.

1. Mr. Kumar is busy this week, but he _____ busy last week.

2. I'm hungry now, but I _____ hungry a few hours ago.

3. Niklas and Adam are at the library tonight, but they _____ at the library last night.

4. Professor Anderson is in her office this morning, but she _____ in her office yesterday morning.

5. It's hot this afternoon, but it _____ hot yesterday afternoon.

6. You're in class today, but you _____ in class yesterday.

7. I'm relaxed now, but I _____ relaxed on the first day of class.

8. We're here today, but we _____ here yesterday.

9. My brothers and sisters are at the beach today, but they _____ there yesterday.

10. There is a basketball game tonight, but there _____ one last night.

Directions: Use the words in *italics* to make questions. Then give short answers.

Example: (*Rodney \ at the tennis courts \ yesterday*)

A: _____ Was Rodney at the tennis courts yesterday _____ ?

B: Yes, _____ he was _____ .

1. (*Kazu and Keiko \ in Madrid \ last month*)

   A: _____ ?

   B: No, _____ .

2. (*the weather in Seattle \ sunny \ yesterday*)

   A: _____ ?

   B: No, _____ .

3. (*you and Robin \ at a party \ last night*)

   A: _____ ?

   B: Yes, _____ .

4. (*Mrs. Masson \ your teacher \ last year*)

   A: _____ ?

   B: Yes, _____ .

5. (*you \ at the concert \ last weekend*)

   A: _____ ?

   B: No, _____ .

Directions: Use the words in *italics* to make questions. Give short answers where needed.

Example: (*Simon \ at the swimming pool \ yesterday*)

    A: _____ Was Simon at the swimming pool yesterday _____?

    B: No, __ he wasn't __.

    A: Where _____ was he _____?

    B: At the beach.

1. (*Martha \ on vacation \ last week*)

    A: _____?

    B: Yes, _____.

    A: Where _____?

    B: Hawaii!

2. (*you \ at the library \ yesterday afternoon*)

    A: _____?

    B: No, _____.

    A: Where _____?

    B: I was at the computer lab.

3. (*you and Edith \ late for class \ yesterday*)

    A: _____?

    B: Yes, _____.

    A: Where _____?

    B: We were at the bookstore.

4. (*Wesley \ in town \ last weekend*)

    A: _____?

    B: No, _____.

    A: Where _____?

    B: On a camping trip.

5. (*the children \ at the zoo \ yesterday*)

    A: _____?

    B: No, _____.

    A: Where _____?

    B: At the playground.

Directions: Use the words in *italics* to make questions. Then give short answers. Use the simple present or the simple past of *be*.

Example: (*Sam \ in class \ yesterday*)

A: _____*Was Sam in class yesterday*_____?

B: No, ___*he wasn't*___.

1. (*Linda \ absent from class \ yesterday*)

A: _____?

B: Yes, _____.

2. (*Linda \ in class \ today*)

A: _____?

B: No, _____.

3. (*you \ nervous \ right now*)

A: _____?

B: No, _____.

4. (*you \ nervous \ on the first day of class*)

A: _____?

B: Yes, _____.

5. (*Olivia \ in Miami \ last summer*)

A: _____?

B: Yes, _____.

6. (*the weather in Miami \ usually \ hot \ in the summer*)

A: _____?

B: Yes, _____.

7. (*Omar and Zahra \ in town \ last week*)

A: _____?

B: No, _____.

8. (*Omar and Zahra \ out of town \ this week*)

A: _____?

B: No, _____. They're in town.

The Past of Be: Review (Charts 8-1 and 8-2)

Directions: Complete the sentences with **was** or **were**. The first one is an example.

SITUATION: *Stormy Weather*

Yesterday, there _____*was*_____ a terrible storm in our town. The wind

_____ blowing, and it _____ raining for hours. I _____ not
     1   2   3

scared, but my little brother _____ really scared by the strong wind. After
                                   4

the storm, there _____ a lot of water in the streets, and there _____
                 5   6

many trees on the ground. Because of the storm, the roads _____ closed.
                                                     7

I _____ happy because my parents _____ not at work. We
  8   9

_____ lucky to be all together and safe at home.
   10

The Simple Past: Using -ed (Chart 8-4)

Directions: Complete the sentences with verbs from the list. Use the simple present or the simple past. The first one is an example.

SITUATION: *Free Time Activities*

listen	play	talk	✓use	visit	watch

1. Svetlana usually _____*uses*_____ her computer to surf the Internet, but last night she
_____*used*_____ it to send some emails.

2. I rarely _____ movies in the afternoon, but yesterday afternoon I
_____ two movies.

3. Oscar sometimes _____ card games with his friends. They _____
cards together last week.

4. Fatima and Maya love their phones! They _____ on the phone twice a day.
Yesterday they _____ to each other at four o'clock and at eight o'clock.

5. Last week Yang _____ to a new song on his iPod. He likes the music very
much, so now he _____ to it every day.

6. Last year Krista _____ her sister a few times. Now her sister has a new baby,
so Krista _____ her twice a week.

A. *Directions:* Complete the sentences with *yesterday* or *last*.

Example: _____Last_____ week, Barb was on vacation in Los Angeles.

1. Paulo visited his grandparents in Brazil _____ summer.

2. Lucia listened to music _____ night.

3. Were you at home _____ afternoon?

4. We played soccer _____ Saturday.

5. Amy watched TV _____ evening

B. *Directions:* Complete the sentences with the information given. Use a length of time + *ago*.

Example: Today is Saturday. We played tennis on Thursday.

   We played tennis _____*two days ago*_____ .

1. It's 10:05 now. I talked to Ian at 10:00.

   I talked to Ian _____ .

2. It's October now. I moved to this country last March.

   I moved to this country _____ .

3. Today is Wednesday. Carmen arrived on Sunday.

   Carmen arrived _____ .

4. Today is Monday. It snowed last Monday.

   It snowed _____ .

5. It's 11:00 P.M. now. I finished my homework at 10:00 P.M.

   I finished my homework _____ .

Directions: Complete the sentences with the simple past form of the verbs in *italics*.

Example: We *have* lunch at the Red Bird Café every Friday. We _____*had*_____ lunch there last Friday.

1. I *see* Kimmy at the bus stop every day. I _____ her at the bus stop yesterday.

2. Bao *writes* text messages to his friends every day. He _____ 25 texts last night.

3. I usually *go* to the gym twice a week. I _____ to the gym on Tuesday and Thursday last week.

4. Mrs. Bilova usually *stands* in the front of the classroom. She _____ in the front of the classroom yesterday.

5. Yuko *puts* her phone into her bag every morning. She _____ her phone into her bag yesterday morning.

6. I usually *get* up at 6:00 A.M. I _____ up at 6:00 A.M. yesterday.

7. Joshua sometimes *eats* cereal for breakfast. He _____ cereal for breakfast yesterday morning.

8. Anton often *sleeps* late on Saturday mornings. He _____ late last Saturday morning.

9. Lisa usually *does* her laundry on the weekend. She _____ her laundry last Saturday.

10. Sam often *comes* to school early and *sits* next to Anna. He _____ to school early yesterday. He _____ next to Anna yesterday, too.

Directions: Complete the sentences. Change the words in parentheses to the simple present, the present progressive, or the simple past.

Example: My father usually (*go*) _____*goes*_____ to work at 8:00 A.M., but yesterday he (*go*) _____*went*_____ to work at 6:00 A.M.

1. Sophia (*write*) _____ an email to her grandmother last night. She (*write*) _____ one to her aunt right now.

2. The tomatoes (*be*) _____ cold now because I (*put*) _____ them in the refrigerator two hours ago.

3. It (*rain*) _____ right now. It (*rain*) _____ two days ago too.

4. I (*get*) _____ text messages from my best friend every day. Yesterday, I (*get*) _____ a funny photo from her, too.

5. Ben (*see*) _____ his aunt and uncle last Saturday. He (*visit*) _____ them every weekend.

6. Yesterday evening Laura and Martin (*eat*) _____ dinner at The Driftwood Café. They (*have*) _____ spaghetti for dinner. After dinner, they (*go*) _____ out to a movie. They (*get*) _____ home late and (*be*) _____ tired, but happy.

Directions: Complete the sentences to make them negative.

Example: Bob watched TV last night. → Bob ___*didn't watch*___ TV last night.

1. Mr. Zhou came to our house yesterday. → Mr. Zhou _____ to our house yesterday.

2. I did laundry last Sunday. → I _____ laundry last Sunday.

3. We played basketball last night. → We _____ basketball last night.

4. The packages were ready at 8:00 A.M. → The packages _____ ready at 8:00 A.M.

5. My sisters studied yesterday evening. → My sisters _____ yesterday evening.

6. Olga went to the beach two days ago. → Olga _____ to the beach two days ago.

7. Sue had breakfast yesterday morning. → Sue _____ breakfast yesterday morning.

8. You called me last week. → You _____ me last week.

9. Jorge sat in the back row yesterday. → Jorge _____ in the back row yesterday.

10. The weather was cold last winter. → The weather _____ cold last winter.

Directions: Complete the sentences. Change the words in parentheses to the simple present, the present progressive, or the simple past. The first one is an example.

SITUATION: *Summer Concert*

Every summer, our town (*have*) _____has_____ free concerts. My friends and I

(*like*) _____ to go because the concerts (*be*) _____ usually a lot of
            1   2

fun. Yesterday evening there (*be*)_____ an outdoor concert at the park. A
                                                  3

band (*play*) _____ rock music. They (*have*) _____ two guitar players, a
                      4   5

drummer, and two singers. Some people (*dance*) _____ and everyone
                                                              6

(*enjoy*) _____ the music. It (*be*) _____ a great show. I really
                  7   8

(*like*) _____ rock music, but I (*go, not*) _____ to the concert because
                9   10

I (*have, not*) _____ time. I (*think*) _____ about it now. I
                      11   12

(*be*) _____ sorry that I (*miss*) _____ the concert last night. Now I
              13   14

(*look*) _____ forward to the next concert.
                  15

Directions: Make *yes/no* questions and give short answers.

Example: A: _____*Did you have a birthday party for your daughter yesterday*_____?

B: ___*Yes, we did*___. (*We had a birthday party for our daughter yesterday.*)

1. A: _____?

   B: _____. (*Paul ate eggs for breakfast yesterday morning.*)

2. A: _____?

   B: _____. (*Andrea didn't go to a party yesterday evening.*)

3. A: _____?

   B: _____. (*Wes and Travis camped by the lake last weekend.*)

4. A: _____?

   B: _____. (*Ivan called Clara yesterday afternoon.*)

5. A: _____?

   B: _____. (*We visited our grandparents two months ago.*)

6. A: _____?

   B: _____. (*My sister wrote many texts yesterday.*)

7. A: _____?

   B: _____. (*We saw an interesting bird last week.*)

8. A: _____?

   B: _____. (*Mr. Ross didn't work in his office last Monday.*)

9. A: _____?

   B: _____. (*You and George traveled to Italy last summer.*)

10. A: _____?

    B: _____. (*I didn't sleep well last night.*)

Directions: Complete the sentences with the simple past form of the verbs in parentheses.

Example: Many people (*come*) _____came_____ to the birthday party on Saturday.

1. I was late, so I (*run*) _____ to the bus stop yesterday morning.

2. Hamid enjoys shopping. He (*buy*) _____ a new jacket last Saturday.

3. I missed the bus, so I (*drive*) _____ my brother's car to school two days ago.

4. Mr. Leonard is our English teacher. He (*teach*) _____ us some new vocabulary yesterday.

5. Paula (*read*) _____ a book in English last week. She was proud of herself.

6. Tony and Elena (*bring*) _____ some chips to the party last night.

7. Last Sunday was sunny and warm. Sophia and I (*ride*) _____ our bicycles to the park.

8. Keiko (*catch*) _____ a cold last week. She still isn't feeling well.

9. Joey was very thirsty. He (*drink*) _____ two glasses of water.

10. I (*think*) _____ about you yesterday. I hope to see you soon.

Directions: Complete the sentences with the simple past form of the verbs from the box. Use each verb once. The first one is an example.

```
break        leave       ring        take
fly          meet        send        ✓wake up
hear         pay         sing
```

1. Jenny was sleepy yesterday because she _____*woke up*_____ at 4:00 and she couldn't go back to sleep.

2. Niko's phone _____ a few minutes ago, but he didn't answer it.

3. I dropped my watch on the floor, and it _____. I need to get a new one soon.

4. I _____ Hiroshi to the airport yesterday. He _____ to Tokyo on Japan Airlines.

5. We had fun at the party last Friday. We _____ some Karaoke songs, and we danced.

6. I _____ a lot of bills yesterday. Now I don't have much money in the bank.

7. I'm scared! I _____ a strange noise outside.

8. Ali _____ his teacher an email because he missed class.

9. I just _____ Mrs. Parker a month ago. I don't know her well.

10. Kevin _____ his house at 6:30 A.M. yesterday because he had an early meeting.

Directions: Complete the conversations with the simple past form of the verbs from the box. Use each verb once. The first one is an example.

> | | | | |
> |---|---|---|---|
> | begin | lose | steal | wear |
> | find | say | tell | ✓ write |
> | hang | sell | tear | |

1. A: Did you finish your essay last night?

   B: Yes, I _____*wrote*_____ it on my laptop, and I printed it before I went to bed.

2. A: What did your mom say about your blue hair?

   B: She didn't like it. She _____ me to wash the color out.

3. A: Can you please repeat that? I couldn't hear you.

   B: I _____, "Please close the door."

4. A: What happened? Why are the police here?

   B: Someone _____ some money from the bank.

5. A: What time did your basketball game begin?

   B: It _____ at 7:00 P.M. and ended at around 9:00 P.M.

   A: Did your team win?

   B: No, we didn't. We _____ by 2 points.

6. A: Where's my jacket?

   B: I _____ it in the closet.

   A: Oh, thank you.

7. A: I need some new shoes, but I can't find any I like.

   B: You should try Martin's. I _____ some shoes there last week.

   I _____ them to work and they were very comfortable.

8. A: Can I borrow your camera?

   B: Oh, I don't have it any more. I _____ it to my cousin for $50.

9. A: There's a hole in your pants. What happened?

   B: I _____ them on a chair at work.

   A: I can fix them for you.

Directions: Complete the conversations with *was, were, did, wasn't, weren't,* or *didn't*.

Example: A: _____*Did*_____ you find your phone?

B: Yes, I _____*did*_____ . It _____*was*_____ in my coat pocket.

1. A: _____ Abdul go to school yesterday?

   B: No, he _____ . He _____ home in bed. He _____ feeling well at all.

2. A: _____ Renee and Michel out of town last week?

   B: No, they _____ . They _____ in town.

3. A: _____ Caroline visit you last Sunday?

   B: Yes, she _____ . We _____ very happy to see her.

   A: That's nice.

4. A: Where _____ you yesterday afternoon?

   B: I _____ at a picnic.

   A: _____ you have a good time?

   B: Yes, I _____ . The picnic _____ a lot of fun.

Review: Past Tense Verbs (Charts 8-1, 8-4 → 8-6, and 8-9 → 8-11)

Directions: Complete the sentences with the simple past form of the verbs in *italics*.

Example: dream   I ___dreamed___ about grammar class last night.

1. *write*   Astrid _____ many sentences for homework yesterday.

2. *be*   The weather _____ cold a week ago.

3. *help*   Ms. Porter _____ us last Friday.

4. *see*   I _____ Professor Keene an hour ago.

5. *study*   Fatima and I _____ physics together yesterday evening.

6. *teach*   Ms. Shin _____ three classes last Monday.

7. *leave*   Julie _____ the house five minutes ago.

8. *tell*   Jae _____ me a funny story yesterday.

9. *ride*   My cousins and I _____ horses every day last summer.

10. *enjoy*   We _____ the baseball game last night.

11. *find*   Marty _____ his keys in the refrigerator yesterday morning.

12. *drive*   My father _____ me to school last Tuesday.

13. *get*   Evan _____ up two hours ago.

14. *finish*   We _____ Chapter 7 a week ago.

15. *be*   The teachers _____ in their offices yesterday afternoon.

Chapter Review

Directions: Correct the mistakes.

Example: Ross ~~goed~~ *went* to the grocery store last night.

1. Mari did not in class yesterday.

2. Mrs. Douglas teached us a new song last week.

3. We didn't came to school last week. We were sick.

4. I no finish my homework yesterday evening. I too tired.

5. Did Simone went to the concert yesterday night?

6. Amanda is here now. She arrived before five minutes.

7. Where was you yesterday?

8. Was Francisco missed the bus yesterday morning?

CHAPTER 8–TEST 1

Part A   *Directions:* Complete the sentences with **am, is, are, was,** or **were**.

1. Jasmin _____ tired now. She _____ at a party last night.

2. I _____ in class yesterday. I _____ in class every day.

3. David and Pedro _____ at the library an hour ago. They _____ at home now.

Part B   *Directions:* Complete the sentences with the simple past form of the verbs in parentheses.

1. My father (*take*) _____ my little brother to the zoo a week ago. My little brother (*ask*) _____ a lot of questions about the animals.

2. We (*hear*) _____ a funny joke yesterday. Barbara (*tell*) _____ it to us.

3. Gina (*visit*) _____ her grandparents last summer. She (*stay*) _____ with them for a month.

Part C   *Directions:* Complete the sentences with the words in parentheses. Use the simple present, the present progressive, or the simple past.

1. Anita (*do, not*) _____ her homework right now. Her phone (*ring*) _____ a minute ago. Now she (*talk*) _____ on the phone.

2. The museum (*be, not*) _____ open last Monday, so Rita (*go, not*) _____ to see the new art show.

3. Khaled (*get*) _____ a new computer last week. Now he (*need, not*) _____ to use the computers at school.

4. I (*walk, not*) _____ to school yesterday. I (*take*) _____ the bus. I usually (*ride*) _____ the bus to school.

Part D *Directions:* Circle the correct completions.

1. A: _____ Amy at the library last night?

    a. Did   b. Is   c. Was

  B: Yes, she _____. She was reading.

    a. did   b. is   c. was

2. A: Did you _____ breakfast this morning?

    a. eat   b. eating   c. ate

  B: Yes, I _____. I had eggs and toast.

    a. eat   b. did   c. do

3. A: Where _____ you yesterday afternoon?

    a. was   b. were   c. are

  B: I _____ at the grocery store.

    a. was   b. were   c. are

4. A: _____ you speak to Mr. Tok last week?

    a. Are   b. Were   c. Did

  B: No, _____. He was out of town.

    a. I'm not   b. I didn't   c. I wasn't

Part E *Directions:* Correct the mistakes.

1. Someone stoled my camera a week ago.

2. Paula didn't worked last Saturday.

3. Yesterday night Olga and I studied grammar together.

4. Our teacher was sick yesterday. We no have class.

5. I got your email. It comes yesterday.

CHAPTER 8–TEST 2

Part A *Directions:* Complete the sentences with **am**, **is**, **are**, **was**, or **were**.

1. I _____ talkative in class now, but I _____ quiet on the first day of class.

2. You _____ very shy last year. You _____ friendly with everyone now.

3. Oscar _____ at a concert tonight. He and Beth _____ at a movie last night.

Part B *Directions:* Complete the sentences with the simple past form of the verbs in parentheses.

1. Mason (*cook*) _____ dinner for me last night. We (*eat*) _____ outside.

2. Kate (*meet*) _____ Paul at a party a week ago. They (*talk*) _____ to each other for hours.

3. Alexei (*buy*) _____ a new iPod last week. He (*pay*) _____ cash for it.

Part C *Directions:* Complete the sentences with the words in parentheses. Use the simple present, the present progressive, or the simple past.

1. Mr. Dragich (*wear*) _____ a suit to the meeting yesterday. He (*wear, not*) _____ a suit right now. He (*like, not*) _____ to wear a suit every day.

2. Peter (*sleep, not*) _____ well last night. Now he (*want*) _____ to take a nap.

3. Anna usually (*take*) _____ a bath at night, but last night she (*take*) _____ a shower instead.

4. The children (*play, not*) _____ at the park yesterday because the weather (*be, not*) _____ very good. They (*play*) _____ video games instead.

Part D   *Directions:* Circle the correct completions.

1. A: _____ Ted in Bangkok a week ago?

    a. Is   b. Did   c. Was

    B: Yes, he _____. He travelled there on business.

    a. did   b. was   c. is

2. A: _____ Meg stay home yesterday evening?

    a. Did   b. Is   c. Was

    B: No, she _____. She went out with her friends.

    a. wasn't   b. isn't   c. didn't

3. A: _____ you tired last night?

    a. Were   b. Are   c. Did

    B: No, _____.

    a. I'm not   b. I wasn't   c. I didn't

4. A: Did people _____ at the party last Friday?

    a. sing   b. sang   c. singing

    B: Yes, they _____. They had fun.

    a. were   b. are   c. did

Part E   *Directions:* Correct the mistakes.

1. Patricia bringed her friends to the picnic last Saturday.

2. Ali is here now. He came before five minutes.

3. I didn't saw Bruno at school last week. He was sick.

4. A lot of students wasn't ready for the practice test yesterday.

5. Where you were last night? You didn't answer your phone.

Expressing Past Time, Part 2

Past Tense Questions with *Where, Why, When,* and *What Time* (Chart 9-1)

A. *Directions:* Read the paragraph and complete the questions. Use the past tense. The first one is an example.

Sasha and Isabella had a party last weekend. It was Sasha's birthday, so they invited some friends to their apartment. Their friends arrived at 7:30 P.M., and they stayed until midnight. Everyone had a good time.

1. A: When _____*did Sasha and Isabella have*_____ the party?

   B: On Saturday.

2. A: Where _____ the party?

   B: At Sasha and Isabella's apartment.

3. A: Why _____ friends to their

   apartment?

   B: Because it was Sasha's birthday.

4. A: What time _____?

   B: The party started at 7:30 P.M.

5. A: When _____ home?

   B: At midnight.

6. A: Why _____ until midnight?

   B: Because everyone had a good time.

B. *Directions:* Complete the negative questions.

Example: A: I didn't sleep well last night.

   B: Why didn't _____*you sleep well*_____?

   A: Because I drank too much coffee yesterday.

1. A: We didn't watch a movie last night.

   B: Why didn't _____?

   A: Because we were too tired.

2. A: My sister didn't study at the university last semester.

   B: Why didn't _____?

   A: Because she was on a trip in Europe.

3. A: I didn't charge my phone yesterday.

   B: Why didn't _____?

   A: Because I couldn't find the charger.

4. A: Jorge didn't do his laundry last week.

   B: Why didn't _____?

   A: Because the washing machine needed repairs.

5. A: Marco and Luisa didn't finish their homework yesterday.

   B: Why didn't _____?

   A: Because they didn't understand how to do it.

QUIZ 2 **Questions with *What* and Yes/No Questions** (Chart 9-2)

Directions: Make questions.

Examples: A: _____*Does Kate usually have a salad for lunch*_____?

   B: Yes, she does. (*Kate usually has a salad for lunch.*)

   A: _____*What does Kate usually have for lunch*_____?

   B: A salad. (*Kate usually has a salad for lunch.*)

1. A: _____?

   B: Pizza. (*Tony and Anita ate pizza for dinner.*)

2. A: _____?

   B: Yes, they did. (*Tony and Anita ate pizza for dinner.*)

3. A: _____?

   B: Yes, he does. (*Jin usually has noodles for lunch.*)

4. A: _____?

   B: A bowl of noodles. (*Jin usually has a bowl of noodles for lunch.*)

5. A: _____?

   B: Yes, I did. (*I got an iPad.*)

6. A: _____?

   B: An iPad. (*I got an iPad.*)

7. A: _____?

   B: "Ten years." (Decade *means "ten years."*)

8. A: _____?

   B: No, it doesn't. (Muggy *doesn't mean "funny."*) It means "hot and humid."

9. A: _____?

   B: Talking on the phone. (*Marissa is talking on the phone.*)

10. A: _____?

    B: Yes, she is. (*Marissa is talking on the phone.*)

A. *Directions:* Make questions with ***who***.

Example: A: _____Who cooked the dinner_____?

B: Jason. (*Jason cooked the dinner.*)

1. A: _____?

   B: My classmates. (*My classmates came to the party.*)

2. A: _____?

   B: Arturo. (*Diana met Arturo.*)

3. A: _____?

   B: Tasha. (*Tasha saved a lot of money.*)

4. A: _____?

   B: Francisco. (*Helena came with Francisco.*)

5. A: _____?

   B: Pedro. (*I'm studying with Pedro.*)

6. A: _____?

   B: Pat. (*Pat gave me a ride to school.*)

B. *Directions:* Make questions and write the answers.

Example: Donna helped Jason.

   a. Who helped _____Jason_____? _____Donna._____

   b. Who did _____Donna help_____? _____Jason._____

1. Maria took a photo of Laurent.

   a. Who took _____? _____

   b. Who did _____? _____

2. Nina emailed Ibrahim.

   a. Who did _____? _____

   b. Who emailed _____? _____

3. The police caught the thief.

   a. Who caught _____? _____

   b. Who did _____? _____

4. Ms. West taught the students English.

   a. Who did _____? _____

   b. Who taught _____? _____

Directions: Make questions. Use *where, when, what time, why, what,* or *who.*

Example: A: _____Why did Marcello take the TOEFL test_____?

B: Because he wants to study in the US. (*Marcello took the TOEFL test because he wants to study in the US.*)

1. A: _____?

   B: Last summer. (*Alex went to Greece last summer.*)

2. A: _____?

   B: A suit. (*Eduard wore a suit to the meeting.*)

3. A: _____?

   B: To the zoo. (*The children went to the zoo yesterday.*)

4. A: _____?

   B: At around 7:30. (*The baby went to sleep at around 7:30.*)

5. A: _____?

   B: Because she needed to finish her homework. (*Monica stayed up late because she needed to finish her homework.*)

6. A: _____?

   B: Willem. (*Willem asked a question.*)

7. A: _____?

   B: Some interesting pictures. (*I saw some interesting pictures at the museum.*)

8. A: _____?

   B: In the cafeteria. (*Frida ate lunch in the cafeteria.*)

9. A: _____?

   B: At 8:00 A.M. (*Math class started at 8:00 A.M.*)

10. A: _____?

    B: Amara. (*I saw Amara at the gym.*)

Directions: Complete the sentences with the simple past form of the verbs in parentheses.

Example: I read a story in English last night. I (*understand*) _____understood_____ all
the words in it.

1. Yesterday I (*hurt*) _____ my hand. My sister (*shut*)
   _____ the car door on my fingers.

2. Joe (*forget*) _____ to bring his wallet to school yesterday,
   so I (*lend*) _____ him ten dollars for lunch. He (*spend*)
   _____ it on soup and a sandwich.

3. Last year James had an accident. His car (*hit*) _____ a bus. It (*cost*)
   _____ several thousand dollars to repair it.

4. Yesterday was Olivia's birthday. We (*give*) _____ her a present and
   some flowers. Anita (*make*) _____ a birthday cake for her. We (*cut*)
   _____ the cake into twelve pieces.

Directions: Complete the sentences with the simple past form of the verbs in
parentheses.

Example: A: Do you know Lucio's Restaurant?

        B: Yes. We (*have*) _____had_____ lunch there last Friday.

1. A: What did you and Dina do last night?
   B: We played a card game. Dina (*win*) _____ .

2. A: Are you taking art class?
   B: Yes, I am. Yesterday I (*draw*) _____ a picture of my mom.

3. A: Do your little brothers like swimming?
   B: Yes! Last summer they (*swim*) _____ in the pool at the park every day.

4. A: Was there any damage from the storm yesterday?
   B: No. The wind (*blow*) _____ hard, and a lot of rain (*fall*) _____ ,
   but there wasn't any damage.

5. A: How did Jenny do on her algebra test last week?
   B: She (*know*) _____ how to do all of the problems, so she (*feel*)
   _____ very happy after the test.

6. A: Did your parents have a vegetable garden last summer?

   B: Yes. They (*grow*) _____ carrots and tomatoes.

7. A: I looked through all my photos yesterday.

   B: Really?

   A: Yes, I (*keep*) _____ the best ones, but I (*throw*) _____ many old ones away.

QUIZ 7 **Irregular Past Tense (Group 7)** (Chart 9-6)

Directions: Complete the sentences with the simple past form of the verbs from the box. The first one is an example.

become	bite	feed	hide	shake
bend	build	fight	hold	✓ swim

1. I _____swam_____ at the pool three times last week.

2. Elena _____ a citizen of this country a year ago.

3. The President _____ hands with the Prime Minister at the meeting.

4. My neighbors _____ their own house two years ago. It was a lot of work.

5. Rob _____ a fifty-dollar bill in his desk last week. Then he couldn't find it.

6. My daughter _____ the ducks in the park last Sunday. She gave them bread.

7. A young mother _____ her baby on her lap.

8. A dog _____ our mailman on the leg. The mailman had to go to the hospital.

9. I dropped my phone, so I _____ over to pick it up. Luckily, it didn't break.

10. My brother and I didn't like each other when we were kids. We often _____ with each other.

Directions: Write the simple past tense of the verbs. The first one is an example.

1. arrive   _arrived_

2. buy   _____

3. carry   _____

4. cost   _____

5. drive   _____

6. fall   _____

7. feed   _____

8. feel   _____

9. forget   _____

10. grow   _____

11. hide   _____

12. live   _____

13. lost   _____

14. need   _____

15. put   _____

16. read   _____

17. say   _____

18. sleep   _____

19. smile   _____

20. stay   _____

21. teach   _____

22. think   _____

23. try   _____

24. understand   _____

25. wear   _____

26. write   _____

QUIZ 9   *Before* and *After* in Time Clauses   (Chart 9-7)

A. Directions: In the pair of sentences on the left, write "1" before the first action, and "2" before the second action. Then choose the sentence on the right with the correct meaning.

Example: __2__ Jan opened the door.   (a.) Jan opened the door after she unlocked it.

     __1__ Jan unlocked the door.   b. After Jan opened the door, she unlocked it.

1. _____ Josh started working.   a. Before Josh found a job, he started working.

     _____ Josh found a job.   b. Before Josh started working, he found a job.

2. _____ Cathy made coffee.   a. Cathy drank a cup of coffee after she made it.

     _____ Cathy drank a cup of coffee.   b. After Cathy drank a cup of coffee, she made it.

3. _____ I brushed my teeth.

    _____ I got out of bed

    a. Before I brushed my teeth, I got out of bed.

    b. After I brushed my teeth, I got out of bed.

4. _____ Ali rode the bus home.

    _____ Ali worked at his office.

    a. Ali rode the bus home before he worked at his office.

    b. Ali rode the bus home after he worked at his office.

5. _____ Michael finished his science experiment.

    _____ Michael wrote a report on his science experiment.

    a. After Michael wrote a report on his science experiment, he finished the experiment.

    b. Michael wrote a report on his science experiment after he finished the experiment.

B. Directions: Use the given time word to combine the two ideas into once sentence. More than one answer is possible.

Example: First: The kids sang "Happy Birthday." *Then:* The kids ate the birthday cake. (*before*)

    Before the kids ate the birthday cake, they sang "Happy Birthday." OR

    The kids sang "Happy Birthday" before they ate the birthday cake.

1. *First:* He took the medicine. *Then:* He felt better. (*after*)

    _____

2. *First:* She lived in China. *Then:* She came here. (*before*)

    _____

3. *First:* We ate dinner. *Then:* We watched a movie on TV. (*after*)

    _____

4. *First:* I drank two glasses of water. *Then:* I went jogging. (*before*)

    _____

5. *First:* They came home from school. *Then:* They had a snack. (*after*)

    _____

Directions: Complete the sentences with ideas from the list. Then change the position of the time clause. Pay attention to punctuation.

> when it began to rain   when he went to the grocery store
> ✓ his dog caught it   we saw tigers and zebras
> she broke her arm   when her baby learned to walk

1. When Timmy threw the ball, _____*his dog caught it.*_____

   _____*Timmy's dog caught the ball when Timmy threw it.*_____

2. Faith clapped _____

   _____

3. When we went to the zoo, _____

   _____

4. When Ruth fell on the ice, _____

   _____

5. Kristos bought some orange juice _____

   _____

6. Mr. Wong opened his umbrella _____

   _____

Directions: Complete the sentences with the correct form of the given verbs. The first one is an example.

It's ten o'clock. **Right now . . .**   **Yesterday** at ten o'clock . . .

1. *pay*   I ___*am paying*___ attention.   I ___*was paying*___ attention.

2. *do*   You _____ an exercise.   You _____ an exercise.

3. *read* Tanya _____ a book.   Tanya _____ a book.

4. *rain* It _____ outside.   It _____ outside.

5. *sit*   We _____ in class.   We _____ in class.

6. *talk* Hiro and Jae _____.   Hiro and Jae _____.

Directions: Complete the sentences with simple past or the past progressive form of the verbs in parentheses.

Example: Yesterday evening, I started to read the newspaper at 6:00. I stopped reading

at 7:30. Luisa called me at 7:10. I (*read*) __was reading__ the newspaper when

Luisa called me.

1. Heidi started to clean her apartment at 11:00 yesterday morning. She stopped at
    12:00. Anya came at 11:30. Heidi (*clean*) _____ her apartment when Anya
    (*come*) _____ at 11:30.

2. Francisco and Tony played cards last night. They started to play at 9:00. They
    stopped at 11:00. Oscar arrived at 10:00. Francisco and Tony (*play*) _____
    cards when Oscar (*arrive*) _____.

3. It started to rain at 2:00 yesterday afternoon. The rain stopped at 4:00. I went outside
    at 2:15. When I (*go*) _____ outside at 2:15, it (*rain*) _____.

4. Lauren and Sue watched a movie last night. The movie started at 8:00 and ended at
    10:15. At 9:00, Sue received a text message. Lauren and Sue (*watch*) _____
    the movie when Sue (*get*) _____ the text message.

5. Our class began at 10:00 A.M. yesterday, but Minh was late. He came to class at
    10:07. When Minh (*open*) _____ the classroom door, our teacher (*talk*)
    _____ about our homework.

Directions: Combine the sentences with **while** in two ways. Pay attention to punctuation.

Example: I was driving to school yesterday. My cell phone rang.

_____ *While I was driving to school yesterday, my cell phone rang.* _____

_____ *My cell phone rang while I was driving to school yesterday.* _____

1. We were walking home yesterday afternoon. It started to snow.

   _____

2. Someone knocked on the door. I was taking a bath.

   _____

3. I fell asleep at my computer. I was trying to write an essay last night.

   _____

4. Hyeri was practicing the piano. The lights suddenly went out.

   _____

5. Joshua's calculator broke. He was studying math last night.

   _____

Directions: Complete the sentences with the simple past or past progressive form of the verbs in parentheses.

Example: Linda (*wait*) __was waiting__ for the bus yesterday when it (*start*) _____started_____ to rain.

1. Alan (*call*) _____ me while I (*cook*) _____ dinner yesterday evening. I (*invite*) _____ him to come to my house for dinner. We (*have*) _____ spaghetti and salad.

2. Boris (*forget*) _____ to turn off his cell phone before class yesterday. While the teacher (*talk*) _____, Boris's phone (*ring*) _____. He quickly (*reach*) _____ into his pocket and (*turn*) _____ it off. After class, he (*tell*) _____ the teacher that he was sorry.

Directions: Use the information about Michael Phelps to complete the sentences. Use the simple past or past progressive form of the verbs in parentheses.

Example: Michael Phelps (*learn*) _____*learned*_____ to swim when he (*be*) _____*was*_____ seven years old.

American Swimmer Michael Phelps

1985:	was born near Baltimore, Maryland, USA
1992:	at age 7, began swimming
1994:	joined the swim team at the North Baltimore Athletic Club
1994-2012:	Bob Bowman was his swim coach
2000:	at age 15, was the youngest American to ever swim in the Olympics
2001:	won his first international gold medal
2004:	at age 19, won 6 gold and 2 bronze medals at the Athens Olympics
2004-2008:	studied at the University of Michigan
2005-2008:	was a volunteer assistant swim coach at the University of Michigan
2005:	had a street in his hometown named in his honor: *Michael Phelps Way*
2008:	at age 23, won 8 gold medals at the Beijing Olympics, and set 1 Olympic and 7 world records
2012:	at age 27, won his 22nd Olympic medal at the London Olympics, a new record by any athlete
2012:	retired from swimming

1. When Michael (*become*) _____ a member of the swim team in Baltimore, he (*meet*) _____ Coach Bob Bowman.

2. Bob Bowman (*be*) _____ Michael's swim coach for many years while he (*swim*) _____ in competitions.

3. After Michael (*win*) _____ his first Olympic medals in 2004, he (*move*) _____ to Michigan.

4. He was a volunteer assistant swim coach while he (*study*) _____ at the University of Michigan.

5. Before Michael (*swim*) _____ in the Beijing Olympics, his hometown of Baltimore (*give*) _____ a street the name *Michael Phelps Way.*

6. In 2012, after Michael (*have*) _____ the record for winning the most Olympic medals, he retired from swimming.

Directions: Circle the correct completions. The first one is an example.

1. What time _____ her homework last night?

   a. was Anna finish   b. Anna finished   ⓒ did Anna finish   d. did Anna finished

2. Where _____ lunch yesterday?

   a. did you eat   b. do you eat   c. you eat   d. you ate

3. A: _____ did you see in Chicago?
   B: A lot of tall buildings.

   a. Where   b. When   c. Who   d. What

4. A: _____ did you see in San Francisco?
   B: My aunt and uncle.

   a. Where   b. When   c. Who   d. What

5. A: _____ David lift weights often?
   B: Yes. He lifts weights three or four times a week.

   a. Is   b. Does   c. Was   d. Did

6. Why did Amanda _____ the day at home yesterday?

   a. spend   b. spent   c. spending   d. spends

7. Who _____ to the meeting after school yesterday?

   a. did go   b. was going   c. went   d. goes

8. A: John went to Miami last week.
   B: Oh, really? Who _____ there?

   a. did he visit   b. he visited   c. he visits   d. did he visiting

9. I had two cups of coffee before I _____ to class this morning.

   a. come   b. came   c. was coming   d. coming

10. I heard some interesting news while I _____ to the radio yesterday.

    a. listen   b. listening   c. am listening d. was listening

11. While Danica was walking home yesterday afternoon, she _____ down on the ice.

    a. was fall   b. fell   c. felt   d. fall

12. Please turn the music down now. Your sister _____ her homework.

    a. does   b. is doing   c. was doing   d. doing

13. When I dropped my glasses on the floor, they _____.

    a. break   b. were breaking   c. broke   d. are breaking

14. Last December Yasu _____ to Tokyo to visit his parents.

    a. fly   b. flew   c. is flying   d. was flying

15. While Max _____ a game on his computer last night, his brother called him on Skype.

    a. played   b. play   c. was playing   d. is playing

16. Who _____ in the big house across the street?

    a. live   b. lives   c. does live   d. living

QUIZ 17   **Mixed Verbs Review**   (Chapters 3, 4, and 8, and Charts 9-4 → 9-11)

Directions: Complete the sentences. Use the correct form of the verbs in parentheses. The first one is an example.

SITUATION: *Driving Lessons*

1. Henri (*have*) ____*has*____ driving lessons every Friday afternoon. His lessons always (*begin*) _____ at 4:00 and (*end*) _____ at 5:30. Right now, it (*be*) _____ 4:30 on Friday afternoon, and Henri (*drive*) _____ in the car with his driving instructor. He (*drive*) _____ in the car with his driving instructor at 4:30 last Friday afternoon too.

SITUATION: *Feeding Baby*

2. When Andrea's baby (*wake up*) _____ yesterday morning, she (*feed*) _____ him breakfast. Andrea usually (*feed*) _____ her baby fruit and cereal for breakfast, but yesterday she (*give*) _____ him an egg. The baby (*like, not*) _____ the egg and (*eat, not*) _____ it.

SITUATION: *Windy Weather*

3. While I (*walk*) _____ to school this morning, I (*drop*) _____ my notebook. The wind (*blow*) _____ my homework away. Now I (*need*) _____ to do my homework again.

Directions: Correct the errors.

Example: While I $\overset{was}{\wedge}$ listening to music yesterday, the battery on my iPod died.

1. What means this word?

2. Yesterday I cleaned my room after I come home from school.

3. Why don't you finish your homework last night?

4. I got a phone call while I was wash the dishes yesterday evening.

5. Where Khaled did go after class yesterday?

6. While Winston was playing baseball yesterday, he felt down on the grass and hurt his knee.

7. Who you danced with at the party last night?

8. When we play basketball last Saturday, we didn't won the game.

9. Who did make this cake? It's delicious.

CHAPTER 9–TEST 1

Part A   *Directions:* Write the simple past tense forms of the verbs.

1. throw   _____

2. smile   _____

3. build   _____

4. enjoy   _____

5. cut   _____

6. win   _____

7. teach   _____

8. hold   _____

9. add   _____

10. blow   _____

Part B   *Directions:* Make questions. Use *where, when, what, who,* or *why.*

1. A: _____?

   B: A new backpack. (*Alexander bought a new backpack.*)

2. A: _____?

   B: Because I was sick. (*I stayed home yesterday because I was sick.*)

3. A: _____?

   B: In my room. (*I studied in my room last night.*)

4. A: _____?

   B: Mimi. (*Mimi made the cake.*)

5. A: _____?

   B: At four o'clock. (*Shazia came home at four o'clock.*)

6. A _____?

   B: Ms. Chang. (*I met Ms. Chang at the airport.*)

Part C **Directions:** Complete the sentences with the words in parentheses. Use simple past or past progressive.

1. While my roommate and I (*wash*) _____ the dishes last night, Omar (*come*) _____ to visit. Omar (*help*) _____ us with the dishes. Then we (*watch*) _____ a movie.

2. Before my soccer game last Sunday, I (*put*) _____ my car keys in my pocket. While I (*play*) _____ soccer, my keys (*fall*) _____ out of my pocket. After the game I (*want*) _____ to drive home, but I (*have, not*) _____ my keys. I (*spend*) _____ thirty minutes looking for them before I (*see*) _____ them in the grass. I (*feel*) _____ very happy.

3. Last weekend my best friend and I (*go*) _____ shopping at a big department store. My friend (*want*) _____ to buy some shoes, and I (*need*) _____ a new sweater. My friend (*try*) _____ on about ten pairs of shoes! While I (*wait*) _____ for her, I (*find*) _____ a pair of shoes for myself. After I (*buy*) _____ the shoes, I (*decide*) _____ not to buy a sweater after all.

Part D **Directions:** Correct the mistakes.

1. Tomas lended me ten dollars last week.

2. Who you saw at the library last night?

3. Did Victor went to the grocery store yesterday?

4. Maria was flew to Puerto Rico a month ago.

5. Mustafa didn't answered his phone yesterday.

6. After she goes to bed, the phone rang.

7. Hannah losed her purse on the subway.

CHAPTER 9–TEST 2

Part A   *Directions:* Write the simple past tense forms of the verbs.

1. know   _____
2. ask   _____
3. become   _____
4. plan   _____
5. forget   _____
6. keep   _____
7. hit   _____
8. drop   _____
9. fight   _____
10. think   _____

Part B   *Directions:* Make questions. Use **where, when, what, who,** or **why.**

1. A: _____?

   B: In Los Angeles. (*Song spent last weekend in Los Angeles.*)

2. A: _____?

   B: Because she lost her purse. (*Sam lent money to Nikki because she lost her purse.*)

3. A: _____?

   B: The secretary. (*The secretary answered the phone.*)

4. A: _____?

   B: Two hours ago. (*Katrina left home two hours ago.*)

5. A: _____?

   B: A bookcase. (*Pat was building a bookcase last weekend.*)

6. A _____?

   B: Mrs. Danova. (*Paula sat next to Mrs. Danova yesterday.*)

Part C *Directions:* Complete the sentences with the words in parentheses. Use simple past or past progressive.

1. When Carol (*arrive*) _____ at the party last night, Willy (*tell*) _____ a joke. Carol (*miss*) _____ the beginning of the joke, and she (*ask*) _____ Willy to tell the joke again.

2. While my brother (*drive*) _____ to work yesterday, he (*turn*) _____ on the radio in his car. He (*hear*) _____ a new song by my favorite singer. After he (*get*) _____ home yesterday evening, he (*find*) _____ the song on a website and (*buy*) _____ it for me. We (*load*) _____ it onto my iPod, and I (*listen*) _____ to the song several times last night.

3. I (*have*) _____ a funny experience last weekend when I (*go*) _____ to the beach with my friends. While we (*swim*) _____ in the ocean, a fish (*bite*) _____ my toe. It (*hurt, not*) _____, but it (*feel*) _____ strange. My friends (*believe, not*) _____ me when I (*tell*) _____ them about it.

Part D *Directions:* Correct the mistakes.

1. Why wasn't Maria go to school yesterday?

2. Marco growed up in Brazil.

3. I talking on the phone to Jenny last night when my parents came home.

4. What means *attic?*

5. Who did draw that picture? It's beautiful.

6. Bruno didn't finished his assignments before class yesterday.

7. I burned my finger while I cooked dinner last night

CHAPTER 10 Expressing Future Time, Part 1

QUIZ 1 **Using *Be Going To*** (Chart 10-1)

Directions: Complete the sentences. Use the correct form of ***be going to*** and the phrases from the box. More than one answer is possible. The first one is an example.

bake a cake	go to bed early tonight	take a lot of photos
buy a new, faster one soon	have a glass of water	walk to school tomorrow
get up early	stay home tomorrow	✓ work out at the gym
go shopping	study together after school	

1. James wants to exercise. He _____ *is going to work out at the gym* _____ .

2. My bicycle is broken. I _____ .

3. Rosa is very tired. She _____ .

4. Our computer is old and slow. My parents _____ .

5. Marcel is thirsty. He _____ .

6. We don't want to be late tomorrow morning. We _____ .

7. Kim and Marie have a lot of homework. They _____ .

8. Trish is sick. She _____ .

9. Ricky has a new camera. He _____ .

10. I need a new jacket. I _____ .

11. Natalia's birthday is next week. Her mom _____ .

Directions: Complete the questions. Use the correct form of **_be going to_** and the words in parentheses. Complete the short answers where necessary.

Examples: A: (*Barbara, take*) _____Is Barbara going to take_____ the bus downtown tomorrow?

B: Yes, _____she is_____. The bus leaves at 8:45 every day.

A: What time (*concert, start*) _____is the concert going to start_____?

B: At 7:30.

1. A: (*Julia, work*) _____ in the morning?
   B: No, _____. She has the day off.

2. A: When (*Paul, see*) _____ his family again?
   B: At the end of the semester.

3. A: Where (*you, live*) _____ next year?
   B: In an apartment.

4. A: (*Misun, go*) _____ shopping after class?
   B: Yes, _____. She loves shopping!

5. A: (*they, bring*) _____ potato chips to the party?
   B: No, _____. They're going to bring pizza.

6. A: What (*you, do*) _____ tomorrow?
   B: Sleep! I'm really tired.

7. A: What time (*we, eat*) _____ dinner?
   B: At around 6:30.

8. A: (*Anna and Jose, get*) _____ married?
   B: Yes, _____. They're planning a June wedding.

9. A: (*Jared, visit*) _____ his grandparents next week?
   B: Yes, _____. On Wednesday.

10. A: When (*Laura, call*) _____ the bank?
    B: At lunchtime.

A. Directions: Rewrite the sentences using present progressive.

Example: Many people are going to go on vacation soon.

_____*Many people are going*_____ on vacation soon.

SITUATION: *Vacation Plans*

1. John and Sue are going to take the train to Los Angeles next week.

   _____ next week.

2. Kate is going to leave for Italy in three weeks.

   _____ in three weeks.

3. May is going to drive to Miami on Saturday.

   _____ on Saturday.

4. I am going to fly to Mazatlan tomorrow.

   _____ tomorrow.

5. Bev is going to visit her nephew in Chicago soon.

   _____ soon.

B. Directions: Decide if the meaning is present or future time. Circle your answer.
The first one is an example.

1. Alice is meeting Erika at the coffee shop at 10:00 A.M.	present	(future)
2. I'm leaving soon.	present	future
3. My sister and I are learning how to sew.	present	future
4. Frank is eating lunch later.	present	future
5. Tomorrow I'm taking my driving test.	present	future
6. We are studying Japanese.	present	future

Directions: Complete the sentences. Use *yesterday, tomorrow, last, next, in,* and *ago.*

Example: Mr. Weebe is going to go fishing in Montana _____*next*_____ summer.

1. I visited my grandparents a week _____.

2. My best friend is going to get married _____ two months.

3. Did you play soccer _____ Sunday?

4. _____ afternoon Sandi went to a movie with Rick.

5. Huong met Amanda at a club meeting _____ semester.

6. I'm going to get up early _____ morning.

7. The restaurant is going to open _____ an hour.

8. Nan talked to the teacher before class _____.

9. What are you going to do _____ weekend?

10. I didn't finish all of my homework _____ night.

11. Is Cathy going to work late _____ night?

12. _____ Saturday we're going to have a picnic.

13. I was talking to Suleiman five minutes _____.

14. Olga is going to call me after school _____.

15. _____ two more weeks we are going to have exams.

Directions: Complete the sentences. Use *ago* or *in* with the words in italics. Use numbers or the expressions *a couple of* or *a few*.

Examples: *minutes*   It's 7:55 P.M. now. The program is going to start at 8:00 P.M.

The program is going to start _____ *in a few minutes* _____ .

minutes   It's 11:30 A.M. now. I talked to Robert at 11:00 A.M.

I talked to Robert _____ *thirty minutes ago* _____ .

1. *days*   Today is Thursday. I saw Emma on Tuesday.

   I saw Emma _____ .

2. *days*   The date today is April 2nd. Elena is going to leave for Spain on April 12th.

   Elena is going to leave _____ .

3. *hours*   It's 8:00 A.M. now. I woke up today at 6:00 A.M.

   I woke up _____ .

4. *hours*   It's 5:00 P.M. now. The concert is going to begin this evening at 8:00 P.M.

   The concert is going to begin _____ .

5. *years*   This year is 2013. My uncle moved to Toronto in 1993.

   My uncle moved to Toronto _____ .

6. *years*   This year is 2013. James graduated from college in 2010.

   James graduated from college _____ .

7. *month*   Today is May 1st. We're going to go on vacation on June 1st.

   We're going to go on vacation _____ .

8. *months*   Today is March 15th. Tanya and Max are going to get married on May 15th.

   Tanya and Max are going to get married _____ .

9. *week*   Today is Monday. I have a dentist appointment next Monday afternoon.

   I am going to go to the dentist _____ .

10. *week*   Today is Friday. Johnny went to a birthday party last Friday.

   He went to the party _____ .

Directions: Complete the sentences. Use the words in parentheses. Use simple past for past actions, present progressive for present actions, and ***be going to*** + verb for future actions.

Examples: Right now, it's 9:00 A.M. I'm in the library.

I (*study*) _____ *am studying* _____ this morning.

Right now, it's 10:00 A.M. Jean left home at 8:30 A.M. to go shopping. She's back at home now.
Jean (*go*) _____ *went* _____ shopping this morning.

Right now, it's 10:30 A.M. Rosa is planning to go to the museum at 11:00 A.M.

Rosa (*go*) _____ *is going to go* _____ to the museum this morning.

1. Right now, it's 10:00 A.M. Franz is at his office.

   Franz (*work*) _____ today.

2. Right now, it's 1:30 P.M. Professor Tang's chemistry class begins at 2:00 P.M.

   Professor Tang (*teach*) _____ a chemistry class this afternoon.

3. Right now, it's 3:00 P.M. Rafael's computer design class started at 1:00 P.M. and ended at 2:30 P.M.

   Rafael (*go*) _____ to computer design class this afternoon.

4. Right now, it's 7:00 P.M. The news program began at 6:00 P.M. and ended at 6:30 P.M.

   We (*watch*) _____ the news this evening.

5. Right now, it's 7:30 P.M. The movie began at 7:00 and it ends at 9:00.

   Ted and Mia (*watch*) _____ a movie this evening.

5. Right now, it's 8:00 P.M. Gina is planning to start doing her homework at 9:00 P.M.

   Gina (*do*) _____ her homework tonight.

7. Right now, it's 10:00 P.M. Antonio is writing an essay. He is planning to turn it in tomorrow.

   Antonio (*finish*) _____ his essay tonight.

8. Right now, it's midnight. I just got home from work.

   I (*work*) _____ until late tonight.

9. Right now, it's early Saturday morning. Khaled is at the car wash.

   Khaled (*wash*) _____ his car this morning.

10. Right now, it's late Sunday afternoon. Gloria went to her aunt's house yesterday morning. She came back home a couple of hours ago.

    Gloria (*visit*) _____ her aunt this weekend.

Directions: Choose <u>all</u> the correct time expressions.

Example: Jack is going to call me _____.

      a. yesterday   (b.) in a couple of hours   (c.) tomorrow

1. I'm going to watch a movie on my computer _____.

    a. last night   b. tonight   c. tomorrow night

2. Sara took a trip to San Francisco _____.

    a. last spring   b. in a few months from now   c. next spring

3. Roberto is leaving _____.

    a. right now   b. at 10:00 yesterday   c. at 10:00 tomorrow

4. Ivan arrived _____.

    a. a couple of minutes ago   b. today   c. this morning

5. Is Miwa going to be here _____?

    a. in a week   b. a week ago   c. next week

6. Jenny began exercising twenty minutes ago. She's almost finished. She's going to finish _____.

    a. a few minutes ago   b. in a few minutes   c. in a few more minutes

7. Miguel sent me a photo of his daughter _____.

    a. in a few more days   b. last week   c. a few days ago

8. It's 1:00 P.M. I'm going to go to the bank _____.

    a. this afternoon   b. in a few minutes   c. this morning

9. We're going to a hip-hop show _____.

    a. tonight   b. next weekend   c. now

10. _____ Abdul was living in Cairo.

    a. A year ago   b. Last year   c. A year from now

A. *Directions:* Complete the sentences with the future form of the given verbs. Use ***will***. The first one is an example.

SITUATION: *Party Time*

1. *have*   Everyone _____ will have _____ a good time at the party tonight.

2. *make*   Renee _____ a cake for the party.

3. *bring*   Sam and Ali _____ ice cream.

SITUATION: *Shopping*

4. *go*   We _____ downtown after class tomorrow.

5. *rain, not*   It _____ tomorrow.

6. *need, not*   You _____ your umbrella or your raincoat.

SITUATION: *Weekend Plans*

7. *visit*   We _____ you next Saturday.

8. *arrive*   We _____ around four o'clock.

9. *forget, not* Sasha _____ to bring his guitar.

SITUATION: *Absent from Class*

10. *be, not*   I _____ in class tomorrow.

11. *send*   I _____ an email to my teacher.

Directions: Make questions and complete the short answers. Use ***will***.

Example: A: _____ Will Ming ride his bicycle home after school _____?

B: Yes, _____ he will _____. (*Ming will ride his bicycle home after school.*)

A: _____ What time will he leave _____?

B: He will leave at around 3:30.

1. SITUATION: *Study Plans*

A: _____?

B: Yes, _____. (*Eric will be at the library this evening.*)

A: _____?

B: Upstairs in the computer room. (*He will be upstairs in the computer room.*)

2. SITUATION: *Dinner Time*

A: _____?

B: Yes, _____. (*I'll cook dinner tonight.*)

A: _____?

B: In a couple of hours. (*Dinner will be ready in a couple of hours.*)

3. SITUATION: *Business Meeting*

A: _____?

B: No, _____. (*Rob and Tara won't be at the meeting tomorrow.*)

A: _____?

B: On a sales trip. (*They'll be on a sales trip.*)

A: _____?

B: Next Tuesday. (*They'll come back next Tuesday.*)

QUIZ 10 **Verb Tense Summary: Present, Past, and Future** (Chart 10-8)

Directions: Complete the sentences with the verbs in parentheses. Use present, past or future. Give short answers to questions where necessary.

Examples: Martina usually (*cook*) _____*cooks*_____ dinner for her family.
Sometimes her husband (*help*) _____*helps*_____.

1. A: (*Fatima, call*) _____ Alicia every evening?

B: Yes, _____. They (*see, not*) _____ each
other often, so they sometimes (*talk*) _____ for an hour. They
(*like*) _____ to talk on the phone.

2. A: (*you, go*) _____ on a picnic yesterday?

B: No, _____. Ivan and I (*play*) _____
tennis. While we were playing, it (*start*) _____ to rain. We
(*wait*) _____ for thirty minutes, but the rain (*stop, not*)
_____. We (*finish*) _____ the game
tomorrow.

3. A: It's 9:00 P.M. (*you, use*) _____ the computer right now?

B: Yes, _____. I (*look*) _____ for some
information on the Internet. Tomorrow I (*visit*) _____ a
friend. I (*take*) _____ the bus to his house. Right now, I (*try*)
_____ to find the bus schedule.

A: I (*want*) _____ to use the computer too.

B: OK. I (*finish*) _____ in a few minutes. Then you can use it.

Directions: Complete the sentences with the words in parentheses. Use present, past or future. The first one is an example.

1. Apples and bananas (*be*) _____are_____ fruits. They (*be, not*)

   _____ vegetables. (*a tomato, be*) _____ a fruit or

   a vegetable?

2. I (*be*) _____ at the library yesterday afternoon, but Denis (*be, not*)

   _____. He and Jay (*be*) _____ at the gym.

   (*you, be*) _____ at the gym yesterday?

3. We (*be, not*) _____ at home tomorrow afternoon. I (*be*)

   _____ at the class barbecue, and Eva (*be*) _____

   there too. (*you and Jan, be*) _____ at the barbecue tomorrow

   afternoon?

Directions: Complete the sentences with the verbs in parentheses. Use present, past or future. Give short answers to questions where necessary.

1. A: (*you, exercise*) _____ often?

   B: Yes, I _____. I (*go*) _____ to the gym four

   times a week.

   A: (*you, go*) _____ to the gym yesterday?

   B: No, I _____. The weather (*be*) _____

   beautiful, so I (*go*) _____ running.

   A: (*you, be*) _____ at the gym tomorrow?

   B: No, I _____. But I (*be*) _____ there the day

   after tomorrow.

2. A: (*you, talk*) _____ to Natasha yesterday?

   B: No, I _____. I (*try*) _____ to call her,

   but she (*answer, not*) _____ her phone. Where (*she, be*)

   _____ yesterday?

   A: She (*be*) _____ at the art museum. When

   she (*walk*) _____ into the museum, she (*see*)

   _____ two men carrying a picture. The men were

   thieves, but she (*know, not*) _____ that then. After

   the men (*leave*) _____ the museum with the picture,

someone (*call*) _____ the police. When the police (*come*)

_____, they (*ask*) _____ Natasha a lot of

questions.

B: (*Natasha, be*) _____ at home now?

A: Yes, she _____.

QUIZ 13   Chapter Review

Directions: Correct your mistakes.

Example: We ~~was~~ late for class.

            were

1. I'm no go to go to the grocery store tomorrow.

2. Next weekend my grandmother will makes a cake for my birthday.

3. Did you went to the concert last Saturday?

4. When you will see Ms. Reed?

5. My husband is going to meet me here in a few minute.

6. I will to buy a present for my sister tomorrow.

7. Does Tom will come next week?

8. Yesterday night I watched an interesting program on the Internet.

9. Where Sophia is going to live next year?

10. My friends didn't arrived on time yesterday.

CHAPTER 10—TEST 1

Part A *Directions:* Complete the sentences with the correct form of *be going to* and the words in parentheses. Complete the short answers where necessary.

A: I (*leave*) _____ for school in a few minutes.

B: What time (*come, you*) _____ home?

A: Around three. Gina (*come*) _____ home with me.

  We (*study*) _____ together.

B: (*Gina, have*) _____ dinner here?

A: No, she _____ .

B. OK. See you later!

Part B *Directions:* Complete the sentences with *will* and the words in parentheses. Complete the short answers where necessary.

A: I'm leaving now. I (*see*) _____ you later.

B: When (*you, be*) _____ home?

A: I'm not sure. I (*be, not*) _____ late.

B: (*you, do*) _____ the laundry when you get home?

A: Yes, I _____ . I (*clean*) _____ the kitchen too.

B: Thanks!

Part C *Directions:* Complete the sentences with *yesterday, last, tomorrow, next, ago,* or *in.*

1. Mari and Nikki are going to go shopping _____ weekend. They love to shop!

2. *A Sister Like Her* is not a new movie. I saw it a year _____ .

3. I texted Yuko three times _____ afternoon. She didn't answer me.

4. I'll see you at the party _____ night. It'll be fun!

5. I'm sorry you are sick. I hope you'll feel better _____ a few days.

6. I wonder where Alex is today. He was in class every day _____ week.

Part D   *Directions:* Complete the sentences with the words in parentheses. Use present, past, or future.

1. A: Excuse me. (*the post office, be*) _____ open now?

    B: No, not now.

    A: Oh! When (*it, close*) _____?

    B: Ten minutes ago. It (*open*) _____ again at 8:00 A.M. tomorrow.

    A: OK, thanks.

2. When my phone (*ring*) _____ last night, I (*answer, not*)

    _____ it. I (*want, not*) _____ to talk to anyone.

    I (*want*) _____ to finish my homework.

3. In the winter, it (*be*) _____ usually cold in Alaska. The weather

    (*be*) _____ cold yesterday, and it (*be*) _____

    very cold tomorrow, too.

Part E   *Directions:* Correct the mistakes.

1. Chris will to call me in a few minutes.

2. Where you will spend tomorrow night?

3. Jason going to play computer games with his friends next Saturday.

4. Is Anne will live in New York next year?

5. I'll see you in a couple of day.

CHAPTER 10—TEST 2

Part A **Directions:** Complete the sentences with the correct form of **be going to** and the words in parentheses. Complete the short answers where necessary.

A: What (*you, do*) _____ next weekend?

B: My poor husband (*work*) _____ at home, but I (*take*)
_____ a trip with my sister.

A: Where (*you, go*) _____?

B: To New York. We (*fly*) _____ there on Friday afternoon.

A: You (*have*) _____ a great weekend!

B: Definitely! It'll be much better than my husband's.

Part B **Directions:** Complete the sentences with **will** and the words in parentheses. Complete the short answers where necessary.

A: Hello. (*Professor Stevens, be*) _____ in her office this afternoon?

B: No, she _____.

A: When (*she, be*) _____ here?

B: She (*be*) _____ back tomorrow afternoon.

A: Thanks. I (*come*) _____ back tomorrow.

B: Good. We (*see*) _____ you then.

Part C **Directions:** Complete the sentences with **yesterday, last, tomorrow, next, ago,** or **in.**

1. We are going on vacation to Disneyland _____ three weeks. I'm so excited!

2. Will you be busy _____? I need some help with my Spanish homework.

3. Where is Karen going to live _____ year? I'm going to live in a college dormitory.

4. Our teacher shut the window a few minutes _____. Now it's warmer in our classroom.

5. Did you study for the test _____ night? I did, and I think I'm going to do well.

6. _____ evening we went to the opera. The singing was excellent!

Part D **Directions:** Complete the sentences with the words in parentheses. Use present, past or future.

1. Ben (*meet*) _____ us at the airport next Saturday. I (*talk*) _____ to him about it yesterday.

2. A: (*you, see*) _____ Lydia and Karim next week?
   B: No. They (*be, not*) _____ in town. They (*be*) _____ on vacation in Morocco.
   A: That sounds wonderful!

3. I (*have, not*) _____ time to write an email to my father right now. I (*write*) _____ to him tomorrow. He (*expect, not*) _____ to get an email from me every day.

4. A: (*bats, have*) _____ feathers?
   B: No. Bats (*be, not*) _____ birds.

Part E **Directions:** Correct the mistakes.

1. What time you're going to arrive tomorrow?

2. Maria will takes an important test later this afternoon.

3. Diana's boss won't to come to the meeting with her next Monday.

4. Do you will be in town next month?

5. I not going to go to work tomorrow.

CHAPTER 11

Expressing Future Time, Part 2

May/Might vs. Will (Chart 11-1)

Directions: Complete the sentences to express "possible" or "sure" ideas.
Use *may/might, will, may/might not,* or *won't* and the verbs.

Examples: Yoko (*come, not*) _____ *may not come* _____ to school tomorrow. She's not sure.

Ivan (*visit*) _____ *will visit* _____ his sister in London next month. He
bought his tickets last week.

1. I have some questions about our homework for tomorrow, so I (*call*)

   _____ you this evening. What's a good time to call?

2. Jenna (*go, not*) _____ out for lunch today. She brought her lunch.

3. My school's basketball team is very good. I am sure they (*play*)

   _____ in the championship game next month. My friends and I

   (*watch*) _____ the game. We aren't sure.

4. Mia and Sue (*play*) _____ tennis tomorrow. They're not sure. It

   (*rain*) _____, so they (*check*) _____ the weather

   report to be sure.

5. Next year, Linda (*study*) _____ at the University of

   Washington. She is very excited about being a student there. She (*become*)

   _____ a doctor in the future. She's not sure about that.

6. I (*see, not*) _____ Chris next week. I'm not sure. I think he's going

   out of town.

A. *Directions:* Complete the sentences with *maybe* or *may be*.

Example: It's getting very windy. _____*Maybe*_____ a storm is coming.

1. I want to go to the art museum. This _____ my only chance to see a Picasso!

2. Quentin is late today. There _____ a lot of traffic this morning.

3. A: Where are my sunglasses?

   B: I don't know. _____ they're in your backpack.

   A: I looked in my backpack, and they're not there.

   B: Look in the car. They _____ there.

4. Mr. Hayashi seldom eats fish. _____ he doesn't like it. Or he _____ allergic to it.

B. *Directions:* Rewrite the sentences. Use the words in parentheses.

Example: Eric might need to take an exam on Friday.

   (maybe) _____*Maybe Eric will need to take an exam on Friday*_____.

1. Luisa might be in the kitchen.

   (maybe) _____.

   (may) _____.

2. I might not be home for dinner.

   (maybe) _____.

   (may) _____.

Directions: Rewrite the sentences. Use the words in parentheses.

Example: The weather may be terrible tomorrow. (*might*)

_____ The weather might be terrible tomorrow. _____

1. We might eat dinner at a restaurant tonight. (*may*)

_____

2. Maybe I will go to the science center next weekend. (*might*)

_____

3. It may be sunny tomorrow. (*maybe*)

_____

4. Maybe we'll watch a movie on TV this evening. (*might*)

_____

5. Emily and Joshua might get married next fall. (*may*)

_____

6. I may be in Paris in the spring. (*maybe*)

_____

7. Maybe I will do my laundry in a couple of days. (*may*)

_____

8. Charles may read something interesting online tonight. (*might*)

_____

9. You might feel better tomorrow. (*maybe*)

_____

10. Maybe my parents will go to the opera on Saturday. (*may*)

_____

Directions: Write "1" before the first action, and "2" before the second action. Then write two sentences: one with ***before*** and one with ***after***. Use a form of ***be going to*** in the main clause.

Example: __2__ I open the door.   a. ___*After I unlock the door, I'm going to open it.*___

     __1__ I unlock the door.   b. ___*Before I open the door, I'm going to unlock it.*___

1. _____ I type the email.

   _____ I send the email.

   a. _____

   b. _____

2. _____ The students take the test.

   _____ The students study hard.

   a. _____

   b. _____

3. _____ I read this book.

   _____ I return the book to the library.

   a. _____

   b. _____

4. _____ I take a long trip by car.

   _____ I buy gasoline.

   a. _____

   b. _____

5. _____ The children build the kite.

   _____ The children fly the kite.

   a. _____

   b. _____

Directions: Complete the sentences with the future form of the words in parentheses. Use *be going to*.

Example: When Tony (*get*) _____gets_____ home from work today, he (*play*)
___is going to play___ with his children.

1. I (*call*) _____ Ms. Adams before I (*leave*) _____
   the office this afternoon.

2. After Giovi (*finish*) _____ his homework tonight, he (*listen*)
   _____ to music.

3. Barbara and I (*buy*) _____ some chocolate for Jeff when we (*go*)
   _____ to Europe next month.

4. Before my friend (*come*) _____ to visit me next weekend, I (*clean*)
   _____ my apartment.

5. Dan (*give*) _____ me his old laptop when he (*buy*)
   _____ a new one next week.

Directions: Complete the sentences with the words in parentheses. Use *be going to* or *will* for the future.

Example: If Miriam (*see*) _____sees_____ Sam tomorrow, she (*invite*)
___is going to/will invite___ him to a party.

1. Your parents (*worry*) _____ about you if you (*come*)
   _____ home late tonight.

2. I (*be*) _____ unhappy if we (*win, not*) _____ our
   baseball game tomorrow.

3. If the weather (*be, not*) _____ nice tomorrow, Carlos (*wash, not*)
   _____ his car.

4. If I (*have*) _____ a headache tomorrow, I (*go, not*)
   _____ to class.

5. Carol (*write*) _____ a long email to her parents tonight if she
   (*have*) _____ enough time.

Directions: Decide the meaning for each sentence. Choose the correct answer. The first one is an example.

1. When I drink too much coffee, I don't sleep well. ⟨present habit⟩ future activity
2. When I watch TV, I feel bored. present habit future activity
3. If it rains, I'm going to take a taxi. present habit future activity
4. When you call me, I will answer. present habit future activity
5. After I go to bed, I fall asleep quickly. present habit future activity
6. Before the game, the coach talks to the players. present habit future activity
7. After class ends, he'll send me a text. present habit future activity
8. When it's sunny, everyone feels happier. present habit future activity
9. When I arrive in New York, I'll call you. present habit future activity
10. When I go to the shopping center, I drive. present habit future activity
11. Before she cuts my hair, she's going to wash it. present habit future activity

Directions: Complete the sentences with the words in parentheses. Use **be going to** or **will** for the future where needed.

Example: If the weather (*be*) _____*is*_____ cold next weekend, Masako and
Yuki (*go*) _____*will go*_____ shopping.

1. When Long (*eat*) _____ at Yeh Yeh's restaurant, he (*have, always*)

   _____ a sandwich.

2. I (*visit*) _____ my friend Ruth when I (*go*)

   _____ to Toronto next year.

3. Before Alex (*go*) _____ to bed tonight, he (*drink*)

   _____ some tea.

4. I (*watch, often*) _____ the news before I (*go*)

   _____ to bed.

5. If the weather (*be*) _____ warm on the weekend, we (*go, usually*)

   _____ to the beach.

6. Callie will take her driving test next week. After Callie (*get*) _____

   her driver's license, she (*buy*) _____ a car.

7. If Pippa (*meet*) _____ her friends after class, they (*get, usually*)

   _____ coffee.

8. I (*call, often*) _____ friends if I (*feel*) _____

   bored.

9. When Professor Mann (*talk*) _____, her students (*listen, always*)

   _____ .

10. Anna (*send*) _____ a text tonight when her plane (*land*)

    _____ .

Directions: Complete the sentences with the words in parentheses. Use **be going to** for the future.

Example: A: What (*you, do*) _____are you doing_____ right now?

         B: I (*take*) _____am taking_____ a quiz.

1. A: What (*Laura, do*) _____ right now?

   B: She (*write*) _____ a text to her friend.

2. A: What (*Alex, do*) _____ every Saturday morning?

   B: He (*sleep*) _____ late.

3. A: What (*you, do*) _____ yesterday evening?

   B: I (*study*) _____ grammar.

4. A: What (*you, do*) _____ in math class tomorrow?

   B: We (*do*) _____ many math problems.

5. A: What (*Emilio, do*) _____ last night?

   B: He (*download*) _____ some music to his computer.

QUIZ 10 **Review** (Chapter 11)

Directions: Check (✓) the sentences that are correct. Correct the sentences with mistakes. The first two are examples.

             may be

1. _____ I ~~maybe~~ absent from class tomorrow.

2. __✓__ I always drink a cup of coffee after I get up in the morning.

3. _____ Jesse might don't play soccer next Saturday.

4. _____ What do your children do after school every day?

5. _____ If I'll have a cold tomorrow, I won't come to class.

6. _____ Toshiko may will come to volleyball practice tomorrow.

7. _____ What your sister doing right now?

8. _____ We may take a taxi home.

9. _____ When Yao plays basketball, everyone always will watch.

10. _____ What did they last weekend?

11. _____ If it snows tomorrow, we wear warm clothes.

12. _____ I will finish my homework after I will check my email.

Directions: Complete the sentences with the words in parentheses. Use any appropriate verb form.

Example: Yesterday I (*finish*) _____finished_____ my design project, and next week I (*start*) _____will start_____ a new one.

1. A: The weather (*be*) _____ cold tomorrow.

   B: How do you know?

   A: I (*read*) _____ the weather report online last night.

2. A: Where (*you, eat, usually*) _____ breakfast?

   B: I (*eat, usually*) _____ breakfast at home, but sometimes I (*have*) _____ breakfast in the cafeteria.

3. A: You look terrible! What (*happen*) _____ to you?

   B: Yesterday I (*fall*) _____ off my roof.

   A: (*you, break*) _____ any bones?

   B: No, but I (*spend*) _____ last night at the hospital.

4. A: My iPod isn't in my backpack! I (*lose*) _____ it!

   B: Don't worry. You (*lose, not*) _____ it. It (*be*) _____ right there in your shirt pocket.

   A: Oh, thanks!

5. A: (*you, be*) _____ out of town during vacation next month?

   B: No. I (*stay*) _____ here and (*help*) _____ at my family's restaurant. The restaurant (*be*) _____ busy then.

6. A: Why is the floor wet?

   B: I (*forget*) _____ to close the windows before I (*leave*) _____. The wind (*blow*) _____ the rain in. I (*clean*) _____ it up in a few minutes.

Directions: Choose the correct completions. The first one is an example.

1. A: Do you like to go to the zoo?

   B: No, I don't. When I go to the zoo, I always _____ sorry for the animals.

   a. will feel   c. feeling

   b. felt   (d.) feel

2. A: Where's Hiro?

   B: I'm not sure. He _____ in the computer room.

   a. might   c. maybe

   b. may   d. may be

3. A: Is Emily going to be at the concert this evening?

    B: No. She's sick. She _____ be there.

       a. isn't   c. will

       b. won't   d. might

4. A: When are you going to clean your room?

    B: I'll clean it after I _____ the dog for a walk.

       a. take   c. am going to take

       b. am taking   d. will take

5. A: Is Hanifa going to come to the gym this afternoon?

    B: Yes, she is. She'll _____ us there at three o'clock.

       a. meet   c. meeting

       b. meets   d. to meet

6. A: Is Carlos in town?

    B: Yes. I saw him _____ night.

       a. ago   c. last

       b. yesterday   d. today

7. A: What _____ next weekend?

    B: I'm going to see a show at the Paramount Theater.

       a. did you do   c. are you going to

       b. are you doing   d. do you do

8. A: When are you going to catch the bus?

    B: _____.

       a. A few minutes ago.   c. Yesterday.

       b. Last night.   d. In a couple of minutes.

9. A: What _____ do?

    B: She's a teacher.

       a. your mother   c. is your mother

       b. does your mother   d. your mother is

10. A: Do you think that this assignment is difficult?

    B: Yes, I do. If I get a good grade on this assignment, I _____ happy.

       a. was   c. will be

       b. am   d. be

11. A: Where are you going to go next Saturday?

    B: If the weather _____ nice, I'll go for a walk by the lake.

       a. was   c. is

       b. will be   d. is going to be

Part A   *Directions:* Write sentences with *may, might,* or *maybe*. Use the given words.

1. (*might*)   it / be sunny tomorrow

   _____

2. (*might not*)   I / be in class on Friday

   _____

3. (*may*)   Don / send me a text later

   _____

4. (*maybe*)   Monica / practice the piano after school

   _____

5. (*may not*)   we / be at the meeting tonight

   _____

Part B   *Directions:* Complete the sentences with the words in parentheses. Use *be going to* for the future.

1. When I (*go*) _____ downtown next Saturday, I (*buy*)
   _____ a new phone.

2. I (*call*) _____ you before I (*leave*) _____ for the
   airport tomorrow. I promise!

3. After Masahiro (*get up*) _____ tomorrow morning, he (*make*)
   _____ eggs and rice for breakfast.

4. You (*do, not*) _____ well on your test tomorrow if you (*get, not*)
   _____ enough sleep tonight.

5. If we (*be*) _____ hungry after the show, we (*stop*)
   _____ at a restaurant for something to eat.

Part C   *Directions:* Circle the correct completions.

1. When we (*visit, will visit*) our grandfather every summer, he always (*tells, will tell*) us
   stories.

2. The teachers (*have, are going to have*) a meeting before classes (*begin, will begin*) next
   Thursday.

3. I (*check, am going to check*) my email in a few minutes after I (*watch / am going to
   watch*) a music video.

4. If Mrs. Chu (*has, will have*) a lot of vegetables in her garden, she often (*shares,
   will share*) them with her neighbors.

5. If I (*see, am going to see*) George tomorrow, I (*lend, am going to lend*) him some money.

Part D   *Directions:* Write "1" before the first action, and "2" before the second action. Then write a sentence using the given time word. Use a form of *be going to* in the main clause.

1. _____ I turn on my computer.

   _____ I check my email.

   (*before*) _____

2. _____ Elly reads for 30 minutes.

   _____ Elly goes to sleep.

   (*after*) _____

Part E   *Directions:* Complete the sentences with the words in parentheses. Use *be going to* for the future.

1. A: What (*you, do*) _____ next weekend?

   B: If the weather is good, we may go for a walk in the park.

2. A: What (*the kids, do*) _____ in their science class last week?

   B: They learned about volcanoes.

3. A: What (*your dad, do*) _____ every day at his job?

   B: He writes computer programs.

Part F   *Directions:* Check (√) the sentences that are correct. Correct the sentences with mistakes.

1. _____ The children maybe at the park now.

2. _____ Maybe George will be at the concert tomorrow night.

3. _____ We'll stay home tomorrow if it snows.

4. _____ Rosa will cook dinner after she's going to go to the grocery store.

5. _____ What Pablo going to do next weekend?

Part A *Directions:* Write sentences with **may, might,** or **maybe.** Use the given words.

1. (*may*) the plane from Chicago / be late

    _____

2. (*maybe not*) Jin / buy a new car this year

    _____

3. (*might*) Travis / become a computer engineer

    _____

4. (*may not*) I / get home until late tonight

    _____

5. (*maybe*) Joe and Mia / have a baby soon

    _____

Part B *Directions:* Complete the sentences with the words in parentheses. Use **be going to** for the future.

1. I (*change*) _____ my clothes before I (*go*) _____
    to the art exhibit this evening.

2. Mariah (*go*) _____ to Hong Kong next December if she (*have*)
    _____ enough money.

3. If my tooth (*feel, not*) _____ better tomorrow, I (*call*)
    _____ the dentist.

4. We (*take*) _____ you on a tour of the city when you (*come*)
    _____ to visit us next weekend.

5. After my sister (*graduate*) _____ from college, she (*go*)
    _____ to law school.

Part C *Directions:* Circle the correct completions.

1. Teresa always (*reads, is going to read*) stories to her children before she (*puts, is going to
    put*) them to bed.

2. They sometimes (*cancel, are going to cancel*) classes if the weather (*isn't, will not be*)
    good.

3. After I (*get, will get*) home from work later today, I (*rest, am going to rest*) for a while.

4. When my parents (*are, are going to be*) tired in the evening, they often (*listen, are going
    to listen*) to music.

5. If I (*need, am going to need*) help with this project, I (*ask, am going to ask*) Wai-Ling to
    help me.

Part D   *Directions:* Write "1" before the first action, and "2" before the second action. Then write a sentence using the given time word. Use a form of **be going to** in the main clause.

1. _____ Our teacher tells us the homework.

   _____ Our teacher allows us to leave class.

   (*before*) _____

2. _____ I give some money to my brother.

   _____ I get some money from the bank.

   (*after*) _____

Part E   *Directions:* Complete the sentences with the words in parentheses. Use **be going to** for the future.

1. A: What (*your parents, do*) _____ when they are on vacation?
   B: They play golf.

2. A: What (*you, do*) _____ after you graduate next year?
   B: I hope I can find a good job in London.

3. A: What (*Alexander, do*) _____ yesterday after work?
   B: He met some friends at a café.

Part F   *Directions:* Check (√) the sentences that are correct. Correct the sentences with mistakes.

1. _____ Julia might to move to Miami next fall.

2. _____ The restaurant may be busy tomorrow evening.

3. _____ If we'll have class on your next birthday, we'll bring a cake for you.

4. _____ What do you doing after you wake up every morning?

5. _____ Rick is going to finish his homework before he's going to bed tonight.

CHAPTER 12   Modals, Part I: Expressing Ability

Using *Can* or *Can't* (Chart 12-1)

Directions: Make sentences. Use the given words and ***can*** or ***can't***.

Example: An adult / talk   <u>An adult can talk.</u>

1. Fish / swim _____

2. A newborn baby / talk _____

3. Dogs / ride bicycles _____

4. A rabbit / jump _____

5. Humans / fly _____

6. A cow / dance _____

7. A monkey / climb a tree _____

8. Cats / read _____

9. A bird / sing _____

10. My teacher / speak English _____

QUIZ 2   **Listening for *Can* and *Can't*** (Chart 12-2)

Directions: Your teacher will read the sentences. Write the words you hear. Use ***can*** or ***can't***.

Example: You will hear: Jojo _____*can*_____ speak Japanese.

1. Tim _____ ride a bicycle.

2. Anna _____ write in Arabic.

3. Mehmet _____ sew a button on a shirt.

4. Chris _____ cook Chinese food.

5. Ivan _____ eat with chopsticks.

6. Sophia _____ play the violin.

7. David _____ drive a stick-shift car.

8. Laura _____ whistle.

9. John _____ fly a plane.

10. Vlado _____ touch the ceiling.

A. _Directions:_ Make yes/no questions. Give short answers.

Example: A: _____Can Carol play the guitar?_____

　　　　B: _____Yes, she can._____ (Carol can play the guitar.)

1. A: _____

　　B: _____ (_Kimmy can water ski._)

2. A: _____

　　B: _____ (_I can't come to the meeting._)

3. A: _____

　　B: _____ (_Max can't ride a motorcycle._)

4. A: _____

　　B: _____ (_I can make French toast._)

5. A: _____

　　B: _____ (_Lisa and Roger can dance the tango._)

B. _Directions:_ Complete the questions with **_Where can_** or **_When can_** and the given words.

Example: (_we, go_)　　A: _____When can we go_____ shopping?

　　　　　　　　B: After school.

1. (_I, buy_)　　　A: _____ some cold medicine?

　　　　　　　B: At the drugstore on Platte Avenue.

2. (_you, fix_)　　A: _____ my car?

　　　　　　　B: Next Friday.

3. (_Ms. Lee, meet_)　A: _____ with us?

　　　　　　　B: At two o'clock tomorrow afternoon.

4. (_I, get_)　　　A: _____ a good haircut?

　　　　　　　B: At the salon next to Central Market.

5. (_the boys, help_)　A: _____ me with yard work?

　　　　　　　B: On Sunday afternoon.

Directions: Complete the questions with the given words and ***know how to***. Then complete the long answers.

Example: A: (*Lisa, use*) _____ *Does Lisa know how to use* _____ a digital camera?

B: Yes, she does. Lisa _____ *knows how to use* _____ a digital camera.

1. (*you, play*)

   A: _____ soccer?

   B: Yes, I do. I _____ soccer.

2. (*Mia, make*)

   A: _____ a pizza?

   B: No, she doesn't. Mia _____ a pizza.

3. (*cats, catch*)

   A: _____ mice?

   B: Yes, they do. Cats _____ mice.

4. (*you, fix*)

   A: _____ a computer?

   B: No, I don't. I _____ a computer.

5. (*Tony, grow*)

   A: _____ vegetables?

   B: Yes, he does. Tony _____ vegetables.

Directions: Complete the sentences with *can, can't, could,* or *couldn't.*

Example: Ostriches are birds, but they ____*can't*____ fly. They ____*can*____ run very fast.

1. Katrina is good at sports. She _____ play basketball and tennis.

2. I _____ go to the party last night. I had to work.

3. Omar _____ come to class tomorrow. He is sick.

4. English spelling is hard for me. I _____ spell very well in English.

5. Yoon was sad. He _____ pass his university exams last year.

6. We love living in New York! We _____ go for a walk in Central Park every day.

7. Mike grew up in Japan. He _____ speak both Japanese and English when he was a child. Now he usually speaks English and never speaks Japanese. Now he _____ speak Japanese well.

8. Tom was a very smart child. He _____ do difficult math when he was 10 years old. Now he is a math teacher. Now he _____ teach students difficult math.

Directions: Correct the mistakes.

                         couldn't
Example: Last year I ~~can't~~ understand my English teacher, but now I can.

1. Paloma learned to play the guitar last year. Now she can plays it very well.

2. When I was five years old, I can ride my bike with no hands.

3. We don't have any matches. We can't to light the candles.

4. Could your parents to speak English before they came to this country?

5. Adam is busy after school today. He cann't go to the club meeting.

6. Where we can find a vegetarian restaurant?

7. Freddy don't can wiggle his ears.

8. Could write you your name when you were four years old?

9. I couldn't washed my clothes last night because I didn't have any laundry soap.

10. David can'ts speak Spanish.

Directions: Rewrite the sentences with ***be able to.*** Keep the same meaning.

Example: Chester can't hear well. _____*Chester isn't able to hear well.*_____

1. I can meet you at the library at 3:30 tomorrow.

   _____

2. Toshi and Mika couldn't go to the US to study English.

   _____

3. Dogs can't talk. They bark.

   _____

4. My daughter could read before the age of five.

   _____

5. I can't touch my ear with my elbow.

   _____

6. Can Anya speak more than two languages?

   _____

7. My father can't come to the meeting next Monday.

   _____

8. Could you hear the difference between those two sounds?

   _____

9. You can cook better than me.

   _____

10. I couldn't find my keys this morning.

    _____

Directions: Complete the sentences with *very* or *too*.

Example: The movie was _____*very*_____ good. I enjoyed it a lot.

1. I couldn't finish my homework last night. I was _____ sleepy.

2. The weather was _____ chilly yesterday, but the children played outside.

3. A: Bobby, you can't wear those jeans to school.
   B: Why not?
   A: They're _____ dirty.

4. I didn't eat breakfast this morning. Now I'm _____ hungry.

5. A: Do you know Jim Nelson?
   B: Yes. I like him. He's _____ friendly.

6. A: Are you going to drink that orange juice?
   B: No. It tastes awful. It's _____ sour.

7. A: Did you go swimming yesterday?
   B: Well, I went to the pool, but I didn't go in. It was _____ crowded.

8. Beth can't reach the books on the top shelf of the bookcase. She's _____ short.

9. A: Did you go to Professor Cho's lecture last night?
   B: Yes, I did. I enjoyed it. I thought it was _____ interesting.

10. I can't wear these shoes. They hurt my feet. They're _____ small.

Directions: Check (✓) the sentences that are correct. Correct the sentences with mistakes. The first two are examples.

can Desi

1. _____ Where ~~Desi can~~ buy a raincoat?

2. _✓_ Nathan is a very busy man, but he always has time for his family.

3. _____ I didn't be able to stay at school for the meeting yesterday.

4. _____ I will can help you tomorrow afternoon.

5. _____ I couldn't finished my assignment last night. It was too long.

6. _____ I went to Hawaii last January. I can go to the beach every day when I was there.

7. _____ When can the doctor see me?

8. _____ Ali is very strong. He can lifts his desk with one hand.

9. _____ This curry rice is very spicy. I can't eat it.

10. _____ I wasn't able to talk to my parents yesterday.

11. _____ Alec know how to speak English very well.

12. _____ I could eat a lot of noodles for dinner last night.

CHAPTER 12–TEST 1

Part A   *Directions:* Complete the sentences with *can* or *can't* and a verb from the box.

> buy   drive   fly   hear   read

1. Bees have wings. They _____.

2. That sign is too far away. I _____ it.

3. Please turn up the TV. I _____ it.

4. This pen costs $2.00. I have $3.00. I _____ this pen.

5. Lisa doesn't have a car. She _____ to school.

Part B   *Directions:* Complete the questions with *can* and the given words. Complete the short answers where necessary.

1. A: (*you, speak*) _____ Russian?
   B: No, I _____.

2. A: (*Maggie, ride*) _____ a horse?
   B: Yes, she _____.

3. A: Where (*I, find*) _____ children's clothes?
   B: On the second floor.

Part C   *Directions:* Complete the sentences with *can't* or *couldn't*.

1. Jan _____ send any texts last night because her phone wasn't working.

2. I'm sorry, but I _____ go running with you tomorrow.

3. We _____ watch a movie now because we have to study.

4. Ian _____ text me yesterday. He lost his cell phone.

5. Paulo _____ understand English when he came to this country.

Part D *Directions:* Rewrite the sentences with the given words. Keep the same meaning.

1. (*know how to*)   Eduardo can speak two languages.

   _____

2. (*be able to*)   I couldn't sleep last night.

   _____

3. (*be able to*)   Ms. Lin can call you back tomorrow.

   _____

4. (*know how to*)   Gina can't wiggle her eyebrows.

   _____

5. (*be able to*)   Could you understand the lecture?

   _____

Part E *Directions:* Complete the sentences with **very** or **too**.

1. This book is _____ expensive, but I'm going to buy it.

2. We can't walk from our house to school. It's _____ far for us
   to walk.

3. I'm not going to go to the beach with you. The weather is _____
   cold.

4. I like those roses. I think they're _____ beautiful.

5. I can't concentrate in this room. It's _____ noisy.

Part F *Directions:* Correct the mistakes.

1. I didn't be able to swim when I was three years old.

2. Billy know how to ride a bike.

3. Sometimes I can't to understand the teacher.

4. We couldn't watched the movie last night.

5. Some fish can swim too fast.

CHAPTER 12–TEST 2

Part A *Directions:* Complete the sentences with *can* or *can't* and a verb from the box.

> help   lift   pay   see   teach

1. Students sometimes _____ the board from the back of the classroom.

2. Antonio is a doctor. He _____ people when they are sick.

3. Jean doesn't have any money in the bank. She _____ her bills.

4. My mother knows how to make bread. If you want to learn how to do it, she _____ you.

5. Yang and Lee are strong. If they work together, they _____ this box.

Part B *Directions:* Complete the questions with *can* and the given words. Complete the short answers where necessary.

1. A: (*you, spell*) _____ Massachusetts?
   B: Yes, I _____ .

2. A: When (*Jane, get*) _____ her driver's license?
   B: When she passes the driving test.

3. A: (*Tomas, wiggle*) _____ his ears?
   B: No, he _____ .

Part C *Directions:* Complete the sentences with *can't* or *couldn't*.

1. I forgot to take my glasses to the restaurant last night. I _____ read the menu.

2. Fatima _____ come to the phone now. She's busy with her children.

3. I don't have my keys with me. I _____ start my car.

4. We _____ check our email yesterday because there was a technology problem.

5. Clara _____ meet us for lunch tomorrow. She has a dentist appointment.

Part D *Directions:* Rewrite the sentences with the given words. Keep the same meaning.

1. (*be able to*)   My grandfather could play the guitar very well.

     _____

2. (*be able to*)   Fish can't live on land.

     _____

3. (*know how to*)   Can you write a compound sentence?

     _____

4. (*be able to*)   We couldn't find fresh flowers at the supermarket.

     _____

5. (*know how to*)   My daughter can eat with chopsticks.

     _____

Part E *Directions:* Complete the sentences with **very** or **too**.

1. Gary doesn't like dried meat. It's _____ salty for him.

2. Luis is _____ homesick, but he's going to stay here.

3. We couldn't see the stars last night. The sky was _____ cloudy.

4. Tina never talks to her classmates or the teacher. She's _____ shy to talk to them.

5. We slept well in our hotel room last night. It was _____ quiet.

Part F *Directions:* Correct the mistakes.

1. When I was younger, I can stand on my head.

2. The music is very loud. I can't hear what you are saying.

3. Mrs. Park grew up in Korea, so she can speaks Korean.

4. Is your brother know how to fix a car?

5. Dave will can come to the picnic next weekend.

Modals, Part II: Advice, Necessity, Requests, Suggestions

Using *Should* and *Shouldn't* (Chart 13-1)

A. *Directions:* Complete the conversations. Use ***should*** and an expression from the list. The first one is an example.

> call the police ✓take some medicine
> drive more carefully wash it
> put on a warm sweater

1. A: I have a terrible headache.

   B: You _____ *should take some medicine* _____.

2. A: Someone stole Yuki's tablet computer yesterday.

   B: She _____.

3. A: Jason is cold.

   B: He _____.

4. A: Luisa had a car accident last night.

   B: She _____.

5. A: My car is really dirty.

   B: You _____.

B. *Directions:* Complete the sentences. Use ***should*** or ***shouldn't***.

Examples: Boris is gaining weight.

   He _____ *should* _____ get more exercise.

   Krista's feet hurt.

   She _____ *shouldn't* _____ wear high-heeled shoes.

1. You _____ eat a lot of candy. It isn't good for your teeth.

2. I'm tired of lending my dictionary to Ed. He _____ get his own dictionary.

3. Mike _____ wear those old pants to school. They look awful!

4. I _____ clean up my room. It's very messy.

5. You _____ skip breakfast. You'll get hungry in class.

6. If the weather is nice tomorrow, we _____ have lunch outside.

Directions: Complete the sentences with the words in parentheses. Use a form of ***have*** + infinitive.

Example: A: What are you doing after class today?

B: I (*meet*) _____ *have to meet* _____ our teacher in her office.

1. A: Do you want to go shopping tomorrow afternoon?

   B: I can't. I (*go*) _____ to the dentist.

2. A: What time (*you, get up*) _____ tomorrow morning?

   B: I (*get up, not*) _____ early. My first class is at 10:00.

3. A: Why wasn't Evan at the party last night? (*he, work*) _____ late?

   B: No, he (*work, not*) _____. He was studying for a big exam.

4. A: We can take the bus anywhere on campus for free.

   B: Really? It's free?

   A: Yes. We (*show*) _____ the driver our student ID cards, but we

   (*pay, not*) _____ to ride it.

5. A: Khalid and Sami left school early yesterday because they

   (*drive*) _____ to the airport.

   B: Why (*they, go*) _____ to the airport?

   A: They (*pick up*) _____ their parents.

A. Directions: Complete the sentences with **must** or **must not**. The first one is an example.

SITUATION: *Safe Driving*

1. You _____*must*_____ have a driver's license to drive a car.

2. People _____ use their cell phones while they are driving.

3. If you want to be safe on the road, you _____ know the rules of the road.

4. People _____ drive too fast. They will get a ticket from the police.

5. You _____ pay attention at all times when you are driving.

6. Drivers _____ check carefully before they turn or change lanes.

B. Directions: Complete the sentences. Use **must not, don't have to,** or **doesn't have to**.

SITUATION: *Using the Internet*

Example: One email account is enough for most people. You _____*don't have to*_____ have more than one email account.

1. Young people _____ put too much personal information on web sites.

2. My brother _____ use the Internet to chat with his friends. They text on their cell phones.

3. You _____ share your passwords with other people.

4. On social networks like Facebook, people can communicate with many friends at the same time. They _____ use email.

5. I _____ surf the Internet at work. If I do, my boss will be angry.

Directions: Choose the correct completions. The first one is an example.

1. This plane is going to take off soon. You _____ fasten your seatbelt.

   a. has to   b. must not   c.) must

2. Johnny, you _____ play in the street. It isn't safe!

   a. must not   b. doesn't have to   c. don't have to

3. Most children in the US _____ go to school on Saturdays. It's a day off.

   a. must not   b. doesn't have to   c. don't have to

4. Alice, your hands aren't clean. You _____ wash them before dinner.

   a. have to   b. has to   c. must not

5. If you want to study in a foreign country, you _____ have a visa.

   a. must not   b. must   c. has to

6. The sign at the zoo says, "The animals need special food. Do not feed the animals." This means that visitors _____ feed the animals.

   a. must not   b. doesn't have to   c. don't have to

7. If you want to become a doctor, you _____ go to medical school.

   a. has to   b. must   c. must not

8. My cats are hungry. I _____ feed them soon.

   a. must not   b. have to   c. don't have to

9. Our school has computers for students to use in the library. Students _____ have their own computers.

   a. must not   b. doesn't have to   c. don't have to

10. If Matthew wants to get a good grade in this class, he _____ turn in all of his assignments by Friday.

    a. must not   b. must   c. have to

11. Some offices require men to wear suits to work, but my husband _____ wear a suit to work.

    a. has to   b. must not   c. doesn't have to

Directions: Read each situation. Write conversations with polite questions. Use *May I, Could I,* or *Can I* and typical responses.

Example: SITUATION: *In a Classroom*

Bob and Eduardo are classmates. Bob has a dictionary. Eduardo wants to borrow it.

Eduardo: _____*Could I please borrow your dictionary?*_____

Bob: _____*Yes, of course. Here it is.*_____

Eduardo: _____*Thanks.*_____

1. SITUATION: *At a Professor's Office*

   Professor Costa is sitting in her office. Mohammed is a student. He wants to come in.

   Mohammed: _____

   Prof. Costa: _____

2. SITUATION: *At a Restaurant*

   Jan is a customer. She wants to have a cup of hot tea.

   Jan: _____

   Waiter: _____

   Jan: _____

3. SITUATION: *At Home*

   Alexis and Carrie are friends. Alexis has a new tablet computer. Carrie wants to see it.

   Carrie: _____

   Alexis: _____

4. SITUATION: *At School*

   Anna and Suzanne are classmates. Anna has a calendar. Suzanne wants to look at it for a minute.

   Suzanne: _____

   Anna: _____

   Suzanne: _____

Directions: Read each situation. Make requests and give answers. Use ***Could you*** or ***Would you*** and typical responses.

Example: SITUATION: *At a Restaurant*

Rachel and Beth are friends. Rachel wants Beth to pass her the salt and pepper.

Rachel: _____*Would you please pass me the salt and pepper?*_____

Beth: _____*Sure.*_____

Rachel: _____*Thanks.*_____

1. SITUATION: *In a Hallway at School*

   Karen and Jeff are classmates. Karen wants Jeff to hold her books for a minute.

   Karen: _____

   Jeff: _____

   Karen: _____

2. SITUATION: *In a Dormitory*

   Kenji and Hiro are roommates. Kenji wants Hiro to turn down his music.

   Kenji: _____

   Hiro: _____

3. SITUATION: *In a Classroom*

   Professor Koh is a teacher. Fatima is a student. Professor Koh wants Fatima to turn
   on the light.

   Prof. Koh: _____

   Fatima: _____

   Prof. Koh: _____

4. SITUATION: *At Work*

   Ms. Martin is the boss and Linda works for her. Ms. Martin wants Linda to take a
   package to the post office.

   Ms. Martin: _____

   Linda: _____

A. *Directions:* Choose the best imperative to follow each sentence. Write the letter on the line. The first one is an example.

1. It's very cold outside. ___E___   A. Stop!

2. Your clothes are on the floor. _____   B. Don't forget to bring your wallet.

3. The traffic light is red. _____   C. Don't sit down on it.

4. The cat is sleeping on the sofa. _____   D. Hang them up.

5. You're going to need money and your   ✓E. Please don't open the windows.
   ID card. _____

6. It's time for class to begin. _____   F. Please open your books to page 398.

B. *Directions:* Write 5 typical imperative sentences for this situation. The first one is an example.

SITUATION: Your friend is sick at home with a terrible cold.

1. _____ *Eat some chicken soup.* _____

2. _____

3. _____

4. _____

5. _____

6. _____

Directions: Add *to* where necessary. If *to* is not necessary, write Ø (nothing).

Example: Could you please ___Ø___ pass me the salt?

1. I wasn't able _____ go to the gym yesterday.

2. Joon Kee might not _____ be in class tomorrow.

3. You must _____ improve your written English.

4. Does your brother have _____ wear a uniform to work?

5. May I _____ leave class a few minutes early?

6. You shouldn't _____ leave your class notebook at home.

7. My roommate didn't have _____ study last night.

8. Would you please _____ carry these books to my office?

9. When are we going _____ visit the art museum?

10. I can't _____ finish this report tomorrow because I don't have time.

Directions: Choose the correct completions. The first one is an example.

1. Ben _____ to be at the concert tomorrow night.

   a. may   b. will   ⓒ is going

2. You shouldn't _____ all your money under your mattress.

   a. to keep   b. keep   c. keeping

3. Carmen had _____ her grandmother yesterday.

   a. help   b. to help   c. to helped

4. My apartment is dirty. I _____ it tomorrow.

   a. should clean   b. clean   c. am clean

5. Daniel _____ basketball with me tomorrow afternoon.

   a. will can play   b. may playing   c. might play

6. _____ I please borrow your umbrella?

   a. Could   b. Would   c. Should

7. Raya has _____ to the passport office next week.

   a. to go   b. go   c. going to go

8. We _____ able to come to the meeting yesterday.

   a. not   b. weren't   c. no

9. _____ you have to study now?

   a. Are   b. Were   c. Do

10. _____ you please shut the window?

    a. May   b. Would   c. Should

11. Hyunjin _____ three languages.

    a. can   b. can to speak   c. can speak

Directions: Check (√) the sentence that is closest in meaning to the given sentence.

Example: We might go to London next summer.

_____ a. We will go to London next summer.

__√__ b. Maybe we'll go to London next summer.

1. You must pay income tax on your salary.

   _____ a. You might pay income tax on your salary.

   _____ b. You have to pay income tax on your salary.

   _____ c. It's a good idea for you to pay income tax on your salary.

2. Antonio might be out of town next week.

   _____ a. Antonio needs to be out of town next week.

   _____ b. Antonio may be out of town next week.

   _____ c. It's a good idea for Antonio to be out of town next week.

3. Emily knows how to play the piano.

   _____ a. Emily can play the piano.

   _____ b. Emily will play the piano.

   _____ c. Emily may play the piano.

4. You don't have to feed the dog.

   _____ a. You must not feed the dog.

   _____ b. You don't need to feed the dog.

   _____ c. You should not feed the dog.

5. It's a good idea for us to go to the gym this afternoon.

   _____ a. We may go to the gym this afternoon.

   _____ b. We must go to the gym this afternoon.

   _____ c. We should go to the gym this afternoon.

6. Paula couldn't go to the lecture yesterday evening.

   _____ a. It wasn't a good idea for Paula to go to the lecture yesterday evening.

   _____ b. Paula didn't have to go to the lecture yesterday evening.

   _____ c. Paula wasn't able to go to the lecture yesterday evening.

7. I may be in my office later today.

_____ a. It's possible that I will be in my office later today.

_____ b. I need to be in my office later today.

_____ c. I'm going to be in my office later today.

8. You must not use your cell phone while you're driving.

_____ a. You shouldn't use your cell phone while you're driving.

_____ b. You don't have to use your cell phone while you're driving.

_____ c. Don't use your cell phone while you're driving.

9. It's possible that Marco is at the grocery store.

_____ a. Marco is at the grocery store.

_____ b. Marco might be at the grocery store.

_____ c. Marco should be at the grocery store.

10. Renee wasn't able to buy a new car.

_____ a. Renee didn't buy a new car.

_____ b. Renee shouldn't buy a new car.

_____ c. Renee can buy a new car.

A. *Directions:* Complete the conversations with ***let's***. Use the words from the box. The first one is an example.

> | | | |
> |---|---|---|
> | go to the supermarket | ✓ have tea | hurry |
> | leave by 5:30 at the latest | turn on some music | watch a comedy |

1. A: Should I make coffee or tea?

   B: _____ *Let's have tea* _____.

2. A: What kind of movie should we watch?

   B: _____.

3. A: _____. We're going to be late!

   B: I'm walking as fast as I can!

4. A: Our plane leaves at eight tomorrow morning. What time should we go to the airport?

   B: _____.

   A: Okay. That sounds good.

5. A: It's too quiet in here.

   B: _____.

6. A: We need fruit and vegetables.

   B: _____.

B. *Directions:* Use ***let's*** to write your own suggestions for each situation. The first one is an example.

1. Mikael is in the hospital. _____ *Let's visit him.* _____

2. It's Kelly's birthday next Saturday. _____

3. I'm interested in African art. _____

4. We don't have class tomorrow. _____

5. The computer isn't working. _____

6. It's rainy and cold today. _____

Directions: Correct the mistakes.

Example: My brother is going $\land^{to}$ study medicine next year.

1. If Kim wants to be healthy, he should exercises three times a week.

2. I forgot my dictionary at home. May you please lend me yours?

3. I have to went to the dentist yesterday.

4. The stove is hot. No touch it!

5. My father has to pays a lot of taxes every year.

6. Would you please to pass the hot sauce?

7. Let's going for a walk after dinner.

8. Did you had to go to school yesterday?

9. It's time for the concert to start. Please is quiet.

10. You must to have a passport to travel to foreign countries.

CHAPTER 13–TEST 1

Part A *Directions:* Complete the sentences. Use **should** or **shouldn't** and a verb from the list.

> drive   eat   stay   study   wait

1. Stephen isn't ready for the math test. He _____ more.

2. This fish smells awful. We _____ it.

3. You _____ too fast. You might have an accident.

4. If you have the flu, please don't come to school. You _____ at home, drink a lot of water, and rest.

5. Nan is too young to get married. She _____ until she is older.

Part B *Directions:* Complete the sentences with the words in parentheses. Use a form of **have** + infinitive.

1. A: Lucio (*leave*) _____ tomorrow.

   B: What time (*he, be*) _____ at the station?

   A: He (*be*) _____ there at eight.

2. A: Mai (*go*) _____ to the doctor yesterday.

   B: Why (*she, go*) _____ there?

   A: She needed some medicine.

3. A: Mommy, I don't like this soup. (*I, eat*) _____ it?

   B: No, but eat your meat and vegetables.

Part C *Directions:* Complete the sentences. Use **must not, don't have to,** or **doesn't have to.**

1. If you're a student, you _____ pay to use this gym. It's free for students.

2. People _____ drink dirty water. They might get sick.

3. Jenna _____ come with us to the concert. She can stay home if she wants.

4. We _____ go to the market now. We can go later.

5. When you go to the airport, you _____ forget to take a picture ID. You can't get on the airplane if you don't have your ID with you.

Part D   *Directions:* Circle the correct completions.

1. _____ I please see your dictionary for a minute?

   a. Should   b. Would   c. May

2. I _____ go downtown with you.

   a. am not going to   b. not going to   c. am not going

3. _____ Olga have to work last weekend?

   a. Did   b. Was   c. Does

4. My uncle _____ speak three languages.

   a. able to   b. is able to   c. is able

5. _____ you please help me with these heavy boxes?

   a. May   b. Would   c. Must

6. I wanted to finish my homework last night, but I couldn't _____ it. I was too tired.

   a. did   b. to do   c. do

7. Could you please _____ the window?

   a. opened   b. open   c. to open

8. Your grandfather must _____ this medicine every day.

   a. take   b. takes   c. to take

9. Class is going to start in fifteen minutes. Let's _____ a cup of coffee right now.

   a. getting   b. to get   c. get

10. Please _____ forget your appointment tomorrow.

    a. you don't   b. don't   c. no

Part E   *Directions:* Correct the mistakes.

1. Where you have to go now?

2. Will you can bake a cake for Jin's birthday?

3. If Wang wants to improve his English, he should listens to English on the radio and the TV.

4. Turning off the light please. Thanks.

5. Did Jose had to study last night?

CHAPTER 13—TEST 2

Part A   *Directions:* Complete the sentences. Use **should** or **shouldn't** and a verb from the list.

> ask   brush   carry   spend   watch

1. Children _____ TV for hours every day. It isn't good for them.

2. Joanna buys a lot of things that she doesn't need. She _____ her money on those things.

3. It's a good idea to take care of your teeth. You _____ them after every meal.

4. If you need information, you _____ the librarian. He can help you.

5. Emma _____ those heavy suitcases. She might hurt her back.

Part B   *Directions:* Complete the sentences with the words in parentheses. Use a form of **have** + infinitive.

1. A: Sonya couldn't visit us last Saturday. She (*work*) _____.

    B: (*she, work*) _____ next Saturday too? If she doesn't, maybe she can visit then.

2. A: What do you want for dinner tonight?

    B: You (*make, not*) _____ dinner for me. I (*stay*) _____ late at school.

3. A: What (*we, do*) _____ for homework today? I forgot to write it down.

    B: Answer the questions on page 204. That's all.

Part C   *Directions:* Complete the sentences. Use **must not, don't have to,** or **doesn't have to**.

1. You _____ keep sugar in the refrigerator. It isn't necessary.

2. Keep this key in a safe place. You _____ lose it. You won't be able to open the door without it.

3. Mari got an e-reader last week. She can download electronic books now, so she _____ go to the library any more.

4. You _____ be late for your doctor's appointment. It's important to be on time.

5. You _____ drive fast when there's snow on the road. It's very dangerous.

Part D *Directions:* Circle the correct completions.

1. Let's _____ to the beach tomorrow. The weather is going to be nice.

   a. to go   b. going   c. go

2. _____ please lend me $5.00? I want to buy something to eat.

   a. Could you   b. Must I   c. May I

3. _____ play in the street. It's not safe.

   a. Don't   b. Don't to   c. You not

4. I'm not sure when we will be home. We _____ home late.

   a. should come b. would come c. might come

5. Baoyang is going _____ basketball this evening.

   a. plays   b. play   c. to play

6. Please _____ the dishes before you go out.

   a. washing   b. wash   c. to wash

7. _____ please use your phone for a few minutes? Mine isn't working.

   a. Would you   b. Should I   c. May I

8. Hanna _____ meet us for lunch on Friday. She's busy.

   a. isn't able   b. can't to   c. isn't able to

9. You have a test tomorrow. You _____ study.

   a. should   b. might   c. would

10. You _____ pass a driving test to get your driver's license.

    a. must   b. should   c. has to

Part E *Directions:* Correct the mistakes.

1. Christos can't goes to the soccer game with us tomorrow.

2. I have to went to the post office yesterday.

3. Please stopping talking. I can't hear the movie.

4. Are you have to go to work tomorrow?

5. We will can bring food to the picnic next Saturday.

CHAPTER 14 Nouns and Modifiers

Identifying Modifiers (Chart 14-1)

A. *Directions:* Underline each *adjective* and draw an arrow to the noun it modifies.

Example: Tom's old hat has a hole in it.

1. Her mother always wears red lipstick.

2. I drank a cup of hot tea.

3. Katya lives in the big house across the street.

4. My husband is an honest businessman.

5. You should wear comfortable shoes to work.

B. *Directions:* Underline each noun used as an adjective and draw an arrow to the noun it modifies.

Example: My favorite shoe store is on Robson Street.

1. I bought a pair of garden gloves at J&J Hardware.

2. He always listens to that radio program on Saturdays.

3. Cathleen washed her coffee cup.

4. The hotel room had a window overlooking the park.

5. Alice gets many text messages every day.

A. *Directions:* Complete the sentences. Use the information in the first part of the sentence.

Example: Soup that is made of vegetables is called _____ *vegetable soup* _____.

1. A book about history is called a _____.

2. A store that sells toys is called a _____.

3. Tickets for a concert are called _____.

4. Plants that grow in the house are called _____.

5. A building that has offices in it is called a/an _____.

B. *Directions:* Complete the sentences with the given words. There are two nouns and one adjective for each sentence. Write them in the correct order.

Example: interesting / program / radio

I listened to an _____ *interesting radio program* _____ yesterday.

1. market / small / vegetable

There is a _____ near my house.

2. fruit / fresh / salad

We made some _____ for lunch yesterday.

3. train / trip / long

I took a _____ through Spain last summer.

4. difficult / problem / math

There is a _____ in this assignment.

5. favorite / star / movie

Who is your _____?

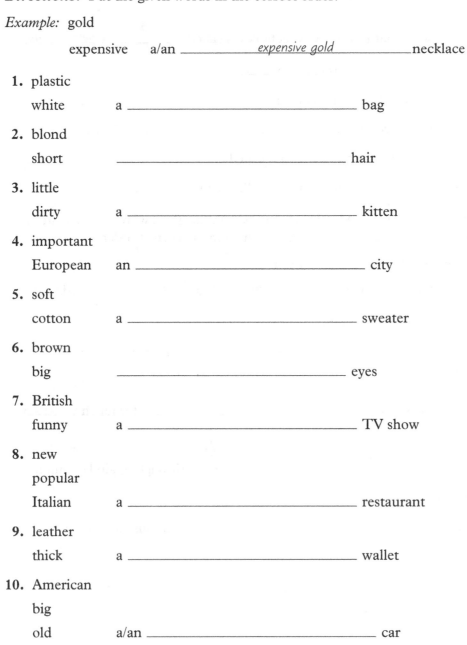

Directions: Put the given words in the correct order.

Example: gold

         expensive   a/an _____*expensive gold*_____ necklace

1. plastic

    white   a _____ bag

2. blond

    short   _____ hair

3. little

    dirty   a _____ kitten

4. important

    European   an _____ city

5. soft

    cotton   a _____ sweater

6. brown

    big   _____ eyes

7. British

    funny   a _____ TV show

8. new

    popular

    Italian   a _____ restaurant

9. leather

    thick   a _____ wallet

10. American

     big

     old   a/an _____ car

Directions: Look at the word order of the modifiers in the sentences. Check (√) the sentences with correct word order. Correct the word order in the incorrect sentences. Make changes in the use of *a* and *an* as necessary. The first two are examples.

1. _____ Tim shouldn't wear that ~~wool ugly~~ *ugly wool* jacket to work.

2. _√_ We had delicious Chinese food for dinner last night.

3. _____ Yolanda is a young woman intelligent.

4. _____ My cousin has big blue beautiful eyes.

5. _____ My grandparents live in a nice old house in a quiet little town.

6. _____ Josh bought a diamond expensive ring for Emily.

7. _____ A middle-aged polite man carried my heavy suitcases upstairs for me.

8. _____ My friends gave me a birthday cake delicious.

9. _____ A school yellow bus stops in front of my house every morning.

10. _____ Kim and Lee share a room in a large red brick dormitory near the stadium.

11. _____ An American friendly student welcomed the new international students to campus.

12. _____ Soccer is an outdoor popular sport in many countries.

Directions: Complete the sentences. Choose a linking verb from the box on the left and an adjective from the box on the right. You will need to use some verbs more than once. The first one is an example.

LINKING VERBS	
feel	look
sound	smell
	taste

ADJECTIVES		
comfortable	confusing	delicious
✓ difficult	dirty	exciting
nervous	proud	sick
sour	wonderful	

1. Carmen told me about her physics class. She has to study for three hours every day for it. It _____ *sounds difficult* _____.

2. I have to take my driving test now. I'm not sure I can pass it. My hands are shaking. I _____ _____.

3. A: Look in this shop window. Do you like those black shoes with high heels?

   B: Yes, but they don't _____ _____. If you try to walk in those shoes, your feet will hurt.

4. I got 100% on my grammar test yesterday. I _____
   _____.

5. A: Are you going to finish your tea?

   B: No. There's too much lemon juice in it. It _____
   _____.

6. Ian told me about a new action movie he saw. I want to see it! It
   _____ _____.

7. A: It's 11:00 A.M. Why are you still in bed?

   B: I have a terrible headache and a fever. I _____
   _____.

8. Ooh! These flowers are beautiful and they _____
   _____. Thank you.

9. I'm going to wash these jeans. I only wore them once, but they
   _____ _____.

10. This chocolate cake _____ _____! I'd like another piece, please.

11. Mike is trying to program our new phone. There are a lot of steps to follow. I'm glad he is doing it. It _____ _____.

Directions: Complete each sentence with the correct form (adjective or adverb) of the given words. The first one is an example.

SITUATION: *A Math Test*

1. *easy*   The teacher gave us an _____*easy*_____ math test yesterday.

2. *quick*   Yasuko finished the test _____.

3. *good*   Most of the students did _____ on the test.

4. *good*   They got _____ grades.

SITUATION: *In the Office*

5. *busy*   Laura works in a _____ office downtown.

6. *neat*   She does all of her work _____.

7. *fast*   She is a _____ worker.

8. *fast*   Laura always talks _____ on the phone in the office.

SITUATION: *English Class*

9. *fluent*   We are learning English. We don't speak English _____.

10. *slow*   Our English teacher always speaks _____, so we can understand him.

11. *quiet*   When our teacher is talking, the students are _____.

Directions: Complete the sentences. Use *all of*, *most of*, *some of*, or *almost all of*.

Example: 2, 4, 6, 8, 10   _____*All of*_____ these numbers are even.

1. ■□□■■■   _____ the squares are white.

2. □■□□□□   _____ the squares are white.

3. □□□□□□   _____ the squares are white.

4. □□■□■□   _____ the squares are white.

5. →↑→↑↑→→→   _____ the arrows are pointing up.

6. ←←←←←←←   _____ the arrows are pointing to the left.

7. ↓↓↓↓↓↑↑↑↓   _____ the arrows are pointing down.

8. ⇧⇧⇧⇧⬇⇧⇧⇧⇧   _____ the arrows are pointing up.

9. K, r, w, P, t, J, c, s, x   _____ these letters are small letters.

10. b, d, r, t, f, j, y, e, h   _____ these letters are small letters.

Directions: Choose the correct completions.

Example: Half of my money (*is,* are) gone.

1. Most of the fruit (*is, are*) fresh.

2. I'm doing my homework now. Half of my homework (*is, are*) finished.

3. All of the strawberries (*is, are*) in the refrigerator.

4. A lot of my classmates (*carries, carry*) backpacks to school.

5. I looked at a web site yesterday. Some of the web site (*was, were*) difficult to understand.

6. Josh looks at several web sites every day. Some of the web sites (*has, have*) interesting information.

7. I asked Mrs. Kuhn for help. Almost all of her suggestions (*was, were*) good.

8. Most of Kate's jewelry (*was, were*) beautiful.

9. We had six math problems to solve last night. Half of the problems (*was, were*) difficult.

10. Some of my classmates (*wears, wear*) jeans to school.

Directions: Choose the correct completions.

Example: Everyone in this class (*speaks,* speak) English well.

SITUATION: *My Favorite Café*

1. (*Does, Do*) everybody want to go to a café now?

2. Everyone (*like, likes*) the coffee at this café.

3. Every (*waiter, waiters*) in the café (*is, are*) very busy.

4. All of the (*person, people*) at that table (*wants, want*) coffee.

5. This café has delicious desserts. Everything (*tastes, taste*) wonderful.

SITUATION: *Taking a Quiz*

6. Every (*student, students*) in this class (*has, have*) to take a quiz.

7. (*Does, Do*) everyone understand the directions?

8. (*Does, Do*) all of the (*student, students*) know how to answer the questions?

9. Everything on the quiz (*is, are*) about English grammar.

10. (*Is, Are*) everybody finished with the quiz?

Directions: Complete the sentences. Use *something, someone / somebody, anything*, or *anyone / anybody*.

Example: There was _____ *something* _____ in my mailbox today. It was a bill.

1. A: Would you like _____ to drink?

   B: No thanks. I just had a glass of tea.

2. A: _____ knocked on my door at midnight last night.

   B: Who was it?

   A: I don't know. I was afraid to look.

3. A: Does _____ have a dictionary? I need to look up a word.

   B: You can borrow mine.

4. A: Mom, I'm bored. I don't have _____ to do.

   B: You can wash the dishes for me . . .

   A: No thanks! I'll find _____ else to do!

5. A: Tomorrow is Susannah's birthday. I want to give her _____.
   Do you have any ideas?

   B: What about a CD?

6. A: Could I use your phone? I need to call _____.

   B: Sure. Here you go.

7. A: Did Ivan tell you about his problem?

   B: What problem? I talked to him last night, but he didn't say
   _____ about it.

   A: Oh? Maybe he doesn't want _____ to know about it. Please
   don't say _____.

   B: OK, I won't mention it.

Directions: Chose the correct completions. Sometimes both answers are correct.

1. A: Who are you going to play with at the concert?

   B: I'm not going to play with _____. I'll play as a soloist.

   (a.) anyone   (b.) anybody

2. A: Did Frank call _____ for the party?

   B: Not yet, he's going to send an email to all of his friends this weekend.

   a. anyone   b. anything

3. A: Do you need _____ from the bookstore?

   B: No, thanks, I have all I need.

   a. anything   b. something

4. A: Did _____ call me?

   B: Yes, your Mom did.

   a. something   b. anybody

5. A: Did you hear that noise? What can it be?

   B: I didn't hear _____. Go back to sleep.

   a. something   b. anything

Directions: Correct the mistakes.

didn't tell
Example: Mr. Jensen ~~told~~ us anything about the surprise party.

1. Our teacher usually opens every windows in the classroom.

2. Would you like a bowl of delicious vegetables soup?

3. Sami didn't eat nothing for lunch.

4. Flora plays the violin very good.

5. I bought a beautiful leather red bag yesterday.

6. Most of the apple are rotten.

7. Our teacher always talks loud.

8. Matt knew anything about the homework assignment.

9. Half of the students in the class speaks Arabic well.

10. We had an easily grammar test last week.

Directions: Choose the correct completions. The first one is an example.

1. This is going to be a great dinner! The food _____.
   a. wonderfully smells
   b. wonderful smells
   c. smells wonderfully
   d. smells wonderful ✓

2. Mr. Jackson doesn't know _____ at his new job.
   a. nothing
   b. anyone
   c. someone
   d. somebody

3. Steve rides _____ to school.
   a. a Japanese small motorcycle
   b. a Japanese motorcycle small
   c. a small Japanese motorcycle
   d. a small motorcycle Japanese

4. Sophia looked at every _____ in the art museum.
   a. picture
   b. pictures
   c. of the picture
   d. of the pictures

5. Abdul went to the mall yesterday, but he didn't buy _____.
   a. something
   b. nothing
   c. anyone
   d. anything

6. A lot of the books in my backpack _____ heavy.
   a. is
   b. are
   c. be
   d. am

7. _____ my classmates are going to the lecture tomorrow.
   a. Almost of
   b. Almost
   c. Almost all of
   d. All most of

8. We had _____ sandwiches for lunch yesterday.
   a. tomato fresh
   b. fresh tomato
   c. tomatoes fresh
   d. fresh tomatoes

9. This soup _____. I can't eat it.
   a. taste terrible
   b. terrible taste
   c. tastes terrible
   d. tastes terribly

10. Almost everyone in my family _____ dark chocolate.
    a. like
    b. to like
    c. liking
    d. likes

11. Our _____ were beautiful and large.
    a. hotels rooms
    b. hotel room
    c. hotel rooms
    d. hotels room

CHAPTER 14—TEST 1

Part A   *Directions:* Complete the sentences. Put the words in the correct order.

1. Italian / shoes / beautiful

   Nadia is wearing ⎯⎯⎯⎯⎯⎯⎯⎯⎯⎯⎯⎯⎯⎯⎯⎯⎯⎯⎯⎯⎯⎯⎯⎯ .

2. modern / interesting / building

   The art museum is in a/an ⎯⎯⎯⎯⎯⎯⎯⎯⎯⎯⎯⎯⎯⎯⎯⎯⎯⎯⎯ .

3. French / old / recipe

   The chef used a/an ⎯⎯⎯⎯⎯⎯⎯⎯⎯⎯⎯⎯⎯⎯⎯⎯⎯⎯⎯⎯⎯⎯ .

4. purse / small / blue / plastic

   My grandmother keeps her money in a ⎯⎯⎯⎯⎯⎯⎯⎯⎯⎯⎯⎯⎯⎯ .

Part B   *Directions:* Complete the sentences. Use the correct form (adjective or adverb) of the given words.

1. *hard*   Isaac is a ⎯⎯⎯⎯⎯⎯⎯⎯⎯⎯ worker.

2. *careful*   It's important to drive ⎯⎯⎯⎯⎯⎯⎯⎯⎯⎯ on the highway.

3. *happy*   Ms. Wilcox looks ⎯⎯⎯⎯⎯⎯⎯⎯⎯⎯ this morning.

4. *quiet*   Luis is a ⎯⎯⎯⎯⎯⎯⎯⎯⎯⎯ person. He always speaks

   ⎯⎯⎯⎯⎯⎯⎯⎯⎯⎯ .

5. *good*   I'm tired. I didn't sleep ⎯⎯⎯⎯⎯⎯⎯⎯⎯⎯ last night.

Part C   *Directions:* Circle the correct completions.

1. (*Does, Do*) all of the (*person, people*) at this table drink coffee?
2. Half of the furniture in my apartment (*is, are*) new.
3. Everybody in the video club (*enjoy, enjoys*) watching movies.
4. All of the students in my class (*is, are*) nice.
5. I watched one soccer game. Some of the (*game, games*) (*was, were*) exciting.
6. A lot of the (*person, people*) in the world (*lives, live*) in Asia.
7. Every (*room, rooms*) in this hotel (*is, are*) quiet.
8. Most of the songs on this CD (*is, are*) beautiful.

Part D   *Directions:* Circle the correct completions. If both completions are correct, circle both.

1. The house is empty. _____ is at home.

   a. Anyone   b. Nobody

2. Linda went to the party, but she didn't eat _____ there. She wasn't hungry.

   a. anything   b. something

3. Hans is in the hallway. He's talking to _____ on his cell phone.

   a. anyone   b. someone

4. My uncle doesn't know _____ about computers. He always needs help.

   a. anything   b. something

5. I need an eraser. Can _____ lend me one?

   a. anyone   b. someone

6. Toshi didn't ask _____ for help with his project.

   a. anyone   b. someone

7. I read _____ interesting on the Internet last night.

   a. anything   b. something

8. Maria didn't tell _____ about her low test grade.

   a. anybody   b. nobody

Part E   *Directions:* Correct the mistakes.

1. I forgot my lunch. Now I don't have something to eat!

2. This chocolate cake tastes sweetly.

3. Susan drives an old black car to work every days.

4. I need to put these flowers in some water. Does anyone have a flowers vase?

5. Some of the people in this room is wearing blue jeans.

CHAPTER 14–TEST 2

Part A *Directions:* Complete the sentences. Write the words in the correct order.

   1. sweater / thick / wool

      Alex often wears a _____ .

   2. tiny / Korean / restaurant

      We sometimes have lunch in a _____ .

   3. ring / old / beautiful

      My mother gave me a/an _____ .

   4. brown / heavy / bags / paper

      We usually bring our food home in _____ .

Part B *Directions:* Complete the sentences. Use the correct form (adjective or adverb) of the given words.

   1. *fast*   Elena speaks Spanish very _____ .

   2. *clear* We're going to go to the beach tomorrow if the weather is

      _____ .

   3. *late*   Calum sometimes comes to class _____ .

   4. *loud*   I heard a _____ noise in the hallway a minute ago.

      Someone was talking very _____ .

   6. *good*   This pizza tastes really _____ . It's delicious!

Part C *Directions:* Circle the correct completions.

   1. Most of the music on this CD (*is, are*) jazz.

   2. Every (*student, students*) at this college (*has, have*) a student ID card.

   3. Half of the money (*was, were*) lost.

   4. (*Does, Do*) every (*teacher, teachers*) in this school give a lot of tests?

   5. All of the (*room, rooms*) in this hotel (*is, are*) large.

   6. Most of the (*vase, vases*) in this museum (*is, are*) from China.

   7. Some of the cheese (*smell, smells*) bad.

   8. Everyone in this room (*speaks, speak*) English.

Part D *Directions:* Circle the correct completion. If both completions are correct, circle both.

1. I didn't talk to _____ last night.

   a. someone   b. anyone

2. Will _____ please help me? I can't open this door.

   a. anybody   b. somebody

3. Did you buy _____ at the mall?

   a. anything   b. something

4. My laptop computer is gone! _____ stole it.

   a. Someone   b. Anyone

5. Maybe John can help you. He isn't doing _____ right now.

   a. anything   b. something

6. _____ told me about the meeting.

   a. Anyone   b. Someone

7. Cara can't cook. She doesn't know _____ about cooking.

   a. nothing   b. anything

8. _____ about that man makes me nervous.

   a. Anything   b. Something

Part E *Directions:* Correct the mistakes.

1. Does anybody want a bowl of hot vegetables soup for lunch?

2. Some of the animals in the zoo is from Africa.

3. My classmate feels sadly today.

4. I need a big bag. I can't carry something in this little backpack.

5. Almost of my friends live in Brazil.

QUIZ 1 **Using *-er* and *More*** (Chart 15-1)

Directions: Complete the sentences. Use the comparative form of the given adjectives.

Example: intelligent Dolphins are _____*more intelligent than*_____ fish.

1. *tall* My sister is _____ I am.

2. *interesting* I think that biology is _____ physics.

3. *busy* The airport in Paris is _____ the airport in Miami.

4. *good* The weather today is _____ the weather yesterday.

5. *cheap* Hamburgers are _____ steaks.

6. *far* My house is _____ from school _____ your house.

7. *noisy* The dormitory is _____ the library.

8. *important* Friends and family are _____ money.

9. *bad* I feel terrible. My cold is _____ today _____ yesterday.

10. *friendly* I like this bus driver. She is _____ the other bus drivers.

Directions: Write the comparative and superlative forms of the given adjectives. The first one is an example.

1. strong   *stronger than*   *the strongest*

2. short

3. funny

4. bad

5. difficult

6. happy

7. big

8. nervous

9. far

10. wet

11. boring

Directions: Complete the sentences. Use the superlative form of the words in *italics*.

Example: Jenny is a _____ *short* _____ girl. She is _____ *the shortest* _____ girl in her class.

1. Joyce wanted a *fast* motorcycle. She bought _____ motorcycle in the store.

2. All the food at the International Food Festival was *delicious*, but the Indian food was _____ food of all.

3. Everyone in Jamaal's family has *curly* hair, but he has _____ hair of all.

4. The weather is very *hot* in this city in July. July is _____ month of the year here.

5. The traffic in Los Angeles is very *bad*. Los Angeles has _____ traffic in the United States.

6. Grand Canyon National Park is very *beautiful*. I think it is _____ national park in the United States.

7. Lake Baikal in Russia is 5,712 feet (1741 meters) *deep*. It is _____ lake in the world.

8. Colorado has some *high* mountains. Mount Elbert in Colorado is _____ mountain in the Rocky Mountains.

9. Soccer is *popular* in many countries. It is _____ sport in the world.

10. There are many *important* international soccer games, but _____ game is the final game of the World Cup. It takes place every four years.

QUIZ 4 **Comparative and Superlative** (Charts 15-1 and 15-2)

Directions: Complete the sentences. Use the comparative or superlative form of the given adjectives.

Example: good In my opinion, Anna's spaghetti sauce is _____*better than*_____ Maria's spaghetti sauce, but Tony's spaghetti sauce is _____*the best*_____ of all.

SITUATION: *The Great Lakes of North America: Lake Superior, Lake Michigan, Lake Huron, Lake Erie, and Lake Ontario*

1. *big*   Lake Superior is _____ of the five Great Lakes.

2. *deep*   Lake Superior is also _____ of all the Great Lakes.

3. *large*   Lake Huron is _____ Lake Michigan.

4. *busy*   Chicago, on Lake Michigan, is _____ shipping port on the Great Lakes.

5. *small*   _____ of the Great Lakes is Lake Ontario.

SITUATION: *Germany's Castles*

6. *beautiful* In my opinion, Neuschwanstein Castle is _____ castle in Germany.

7. *popular*   Neuschwanstein Castle is also _____ castle in Germany.

8. *old*   Hohenzollern Castle is _____ Neuschwanstein Castle.

9. *interesting* In my opinion, castles from the middle ages are _____ newer castles.

10. *scary*   Some people say Eltz Castle has ghosts. It's _____ castle of all!

A. *Directions:* Complete the sentences. Use the information in *italics* and ***one of*** +
superlative + plural noun.

Example: The Missouri River is *a long river*. In fact, the Missouri River is
<u>one of the longest rivers</u>   in North America.

1. Lima, Peru, is *a large city*. In fact, Lima is _____ in South
   America.

2. The Golden Gate Bridge in San Francisco is *a beautiful bridge*. In my opinion, the
   Golden Gate Bridge is _____ in the world.

3. Tokyo International Airport is *a busy airport*. In fact, Tokyo International Airport is
   _____ in the world.

4. Italy is *a good place* to take a vacation. In my opinion, Italy is
   _____ in Europe to take a vacation.

5. Global warming is *a serious problem*. In my opinion, global warming is
   _____ in the world.

B. *Directions:* Use the given phrases to make sentences. Use ***one of*** + superlative +
plural noun.

Example: a good restaurant in (*this city*) <u>Anthony's is one of the best restaurants in Edmonds.</u>

1. a funny movie of (*this year*)

   _____

2. a difficult language in the world

   _____

3. a short person in our class

   _____

4. a famous movie star in the world

   _____

5. an interesting place in (*this country*)

   _____

Directions: Complete the sentences. Use the comparative or superlative form of the given adverbs.

Examples: neat   Karen writes _____more neatly than_____ I do.

         neat   Irena writes _____the most neatly_____ of all.

1. *quietly*   Anna talks _____ Sara does.

2. *carefully*   Chris works _____ of all the people in his office.

3. *late*   My mother usually goes to bed _____ I do.

4. *early*   My father gets up _____ of everyone in our family.

5. *well*   Andreas won our tennis game. He played _____ I did.

6. *hard*   Sonya studied _____ Alice did.

7. *clearly*   Our teacher this year explains lessons _____ our teacher last year.

8. *well*   This computer works _____ of all the computers in the school.

9. *quickly*   Barbara walks _____ of all my friends.

10. *fluently*   Nikki speaks English _____ Max does.

Directions: Complete the sentences. Use the correct form (adjective or adverb, comparative or superlative) of the given word.

Examples: *tall*   The Taipei 101 Building is _____ *taller than* _____ the Empire State Building.

beautiful   Fumiko plays the violin _____ *the most beautifully* _____ of all the students in her music class.

1. *good*   You can paint _____ I can.

2. *quiet*   Mona has _____ voice of anyone I know.

3. *slow*   My computer loads programs _____ my brother's computer does.

4. *fast*   The cheetah runs _____ of all animals.

5. *fluent*   My brother speaks Korean _____ of all the children in our family.

6. *easy*   The test for Chapter 11 was _____ the test for Chapter 12.

7. *funny*   Patrick always tells _____ stories of all.

8. *hard*   Charles studied _____ Julia did.

9. *bad*   That is _____ movie of all!

10. *interesting*   In my opinion, Istanbul is _____ city in Europe.

11. *soft*   This pillow is _____ that one.

12. *careful*   She writes _____ other students do.

13. *loud*   My mother cheered _____ of all the fans at the soccer game.

14. *slow*   I was driving behind _____ driver on the road!

15. *beautiful*   My hometown is _____ this town is.

A. *Directions:* Complete the sentences. Use ***the same*** (*as*), ***similar*** (*to*), and ***different*** (*from*) in your completions. The first one is an example.

Picture A   **Picture B**   **Picture C**   **Picture D**

1. Picture A _____ *is different from* _____ Picture B.

2. Picture B _____ Picture C.

3. Picture C and Picture D _____.

4. Picture A and Picture C _____.

5. Picture D _____ Picture C.

6. Picture B and Picture D _____.

B. *Directions:* Correct the mistakes.

Example: Bats are different ~~to~~ *from* birds.

1. Hans and Paulo's apartments are a same size.

2. Bats and birds are differents.

3. A college is similar a university.

4. My English teacher is very different to my Math teacher.

5. My sister's eyes are the same color with my eyes.

Directions: Choose the correct completions.

Example: Mari and Jane have similar hairstyles. In other words, their hairstyles are
(*like*, (*alike*)).

1. Anne and Emily have similar hats. In other words, Anne's hat is (*like*, *alike*) Emily's.

2. A lemon and an orange are (*like*, *alike*) in some ways.

3. Tomas' phone is (*like*, *alike*) Alex's phone. In other words, their phones are (*like*, *alike*).

4. How is a bird (*like*, *alike*) a butterfly?

5. Ducks are (*like*, *alike*) chickens in some ways, but different in other ways.

6. My new car is similar to my roommate's. In other words, my car is (*like*, *alike*) her
car.

7. Did you know that Greg and his twin brother look exactly (*like*, *alike*)?

8. Guitars and violins are (*like*, *alike*) in some ways.

9. My mom is (*like*, *alike*) my dad. They both want me to get a good education.

QUIZ 10   **Using *But***   (Chart 15-7)

Directions: Complete the sentences with adjectives from the list. The first one is an
example.

boring	early	sad	thirsty
cheap	hardworking	serious	young
✓ dirty	married	sick	

1. My living room is clean, but my kitchen is _____*dirty*_____.

2. Lisa is healthy now, but she was _____ last week.

3. Khaled is lazy, but his sister is _____. She gets very good grades.

4. I'm not hungry, but I'm really _____. Can I have some water,
please?

5. The Ritz Hotel is expensive, but the Youth Hostel is _____.

6. Yesterday the bus came late, but this morning it was _____.

7. My grandfather is old, but I am _____. He's 72, and I'm 13.

8. Margie is a very funny girl, but her twin sister is very _____.

9. The first book in the series was interesting, but the second one was

_____.

10. Miryam is still single, but her brother is _____. He loves his wife
very much.

Directions: Complete the sentences with an appropriate verb, affirmative or negative.

Example: Paul reads the newspaper every day, but Boris _____*doesn't*_____.

1. The sandwiches were good, but the coffee _____.

2. The children don't speak Chinese, but their mother _____.

3. Paula had a good time at the party, but Rob _____.

4. Abdul can't ski, but Toshi _____.

5. These clothes are dirty, but those clothes _____.

6. Ben wasn't at the picnic last Sunday, but Ricardo and Jack _____.

7. I like classical music, but my friends _____.

8. Diana won't be in town next week, but her husband _____.

9. Alex is happy, but Nan _____.

10. Sophia didn't go shopping, but Katya _____.

Directions: Choose the correct completions. The first one is an example.

1. Anna's hairstyle is _____ Joan's.
   a. the same   c. same as
   b. the same as   d. as same as

2. Shin's first language is _____ Paulo's.
   a. different with   c. different from
   b. different to   d. different

3. Heide always drives too fast. Ted drives _____ than Heide does.
   a. more careful   c. more carefully
   b. carefully   d. carefuller

4. Alaska is _____ state in the United States.
   a. the largest   c. largest
   b. the most large   d. the most largest

5. My suitcase is _____ yours. Can you help me carry it?
   a. more heavy   c. heavy than
   b. more heavier than   d. heavier than

6. A new sports car is _____ a motorcycle.
   a. expensive than   c. expensiver than
   b. more expensive than d. more expensive

7. My parents will go to Mexico next month, but I _____.
   a. will   c. won't
   b. do   d. don't

8. Video games and computer games are _____ in many ways.
   a. similar with   c. similar
   b. like   d. similar to

9. Mark worked _____ than Denis.
   a. more harder   c. hard
   b. more hardly   d. harder

10. Montreal is one of _____ in Canada.
    a. the biggest cities   c. biggest city
    b. the biggest city   d. biggest cities

11. Tara has a car, but her brother _____.
    a. don't   c. isn't
    b. doesn't   d. hasn't

Directions: Correct the mistakes.

Example: Mr. Yoon is ~~tallest~~ *taller* than Ms. Shim.

1. Eduardo's backpack is the same mine.

2. Tran works hard, but his roommate don't. Tran's roommate is more lazier.

3. A fly is different to a bee in many ways.

4. Health is more important as money.

5. The weather is more colder this week than last week.

6. In my opinion, the Bluebird Restaurant is worst restaurant in this city.

7. Professor Kondo's tests are difficulter than Professor Lee's tests.

8. Helena sings more beautiful than Gina.

9. Tennis balls and golf balls aren't a same size. Tennis balls are more large than golf balls.

10. The Yangtze River is one of longest river in the world.

11. This art history book is interesting more than that psychology book.

12. Tracy's earrings are similar with yours. In other words, her earrings are alike yours.

CHAPTER 15—TEST 1

Part A   **Directions:** Complete the sentences. Use the comparative or superlative form of the given adjectives.

1. *old*   My mother is _____ my father.

2. *pretty*   I like those roses. I think that they are _____ of all the flowers in the garden.

3. *good*   The food at Toledo's Restaurant is _____ the food at The Lotus Restaurant.

4. *interesting* My history class is _____ my math class.

5. *important*   The computer is one of _____ inventions in the modern world.

Part B   **Directions:** Complete the sentences. Use the comparative or superlative form of the given adverbs.

1. *quickly*   Raoul finished the assignment _____ Ivan did.

2. *clearly*   Patricia explained her ideas _____ of all the students in the group.

3. *fast*   Katrina read the chapter _____ Jeff did.

4. *early*   Pieter arrived at work _____ Roberto did. Tara arrived _____ of all their co-workers.

Part C   **Directions:** Circle the correct completions.

1. Arnie is (*stronger than, more strongly than*) Kent is. He can lift weights (*easier than, more easily than*) Kent can.

2. Maria is one of (*the best student, the best students*) in our history class. She is also (*the quietest student, the quietest students*) in the class.

3. Payton plays football (*the best, better than*) of all the players on his team.

Part D   **Directions:** Complete the sentences. Use an appropriate verb, affirmative or negative.

1. Alex is hungry, but we _____.

2. Rodrigo won't be at the meeting, but Carl _____.

3. Martha calls friends on the Internet, but I _____.

4. The children weren't tired, but their teacher _____.

5. My sister doesn't like coffee, but I _____.

Part E *Directions:* Write sentences comparing the shapes. Use the given words.

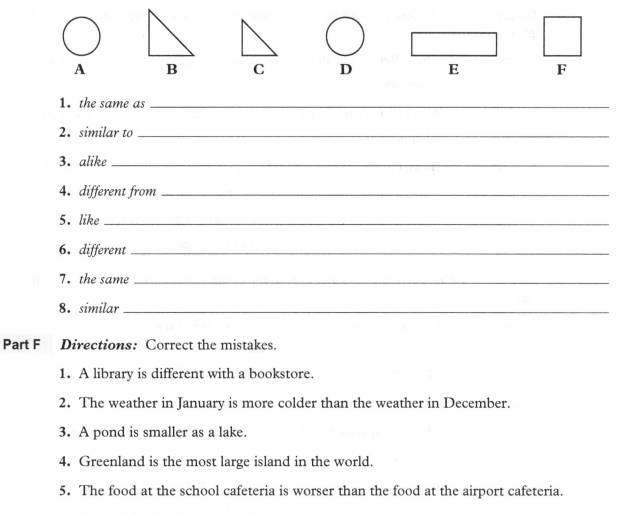

A B C D E F

1. *the same as* _____

2. *similar to* _____

3. *alike* _____

4. *different from* _____

5. *like* _____

6. *different* _____

7. *the same* _____

8. *similar* _____

Part F *Directions:* Correct the mistakes.

1. A library is different with a bookstore.

2. The weather in January is more colder than the weather in December.

3. A pond is smaller as a lake.

4. Greenland is the most large island in the world.

5. The food at the school cafeteria is worser than the food at the airport cafeteria.

6. Spanish is alike Portuguese in some ways.

7. An American football and a soccer ball aren't a same shape.

CHAPTER 15–TEST 2

Part A *Directions:* Complete the sentences. Use the comparative or superlative form of the given adjectives.

1. *famous* The Eiffel Tower in Paris is one of _____ landmarks in Europe.

2. *easy* This test isn't too hard. It's _____ the test on Chapter 10.

3. *expensive* Dinner at a nice restaurant is _____ fast food.

4. *wet* It often rains in the winter here. The winters are _____ the summers. January is usually _____ month of the year.

Part B *Directions:* Complete the sentences. Use the comparative or superlative form of the given adverbs.

1. *slowly* I finished lunch before Jill and Sami did. Jill ate _____. I did. Sami ate _____ of all.

2. *late* Will came to class _____ Boris.

3. *fluently* My sister speaks Spanish _____ of all the people in my family.

4. *well* Joyce cooks _____ her mother.

Part C *Directions:* Circle the correct completions.

1. My new cell phone is (*more colorful than, the most colorful*) my old cell phone.

2. Mary sang (*more beautifully, the most beautifully*) of all the singers.

3. Brad is (*more intelligent, more intelligently*) than his twin brother Benji, but Benji is one of (*the best guitarist, the best guitarists*) I know.

4. The movie I saw yesterday was (*funnier than, the funniest*) the movie we saw last weekend.

Part D *Directions:* Complete the sentences. Use an appropriate verb, affirmative or negative.

1. Yuko has a guitar, but Andy _____.

2. Rie and Hans went to a movie last night, but Elena _____.

3. My boots aren't comfortable, but my running shoes _____.

4. I can't speak Russian, but Natasha _____.

5. Jana will be in class tomorrow, but Mohammed and Carlos _____.

Part E *Directions:* Write sentences comparing the shapes. Use the given words.

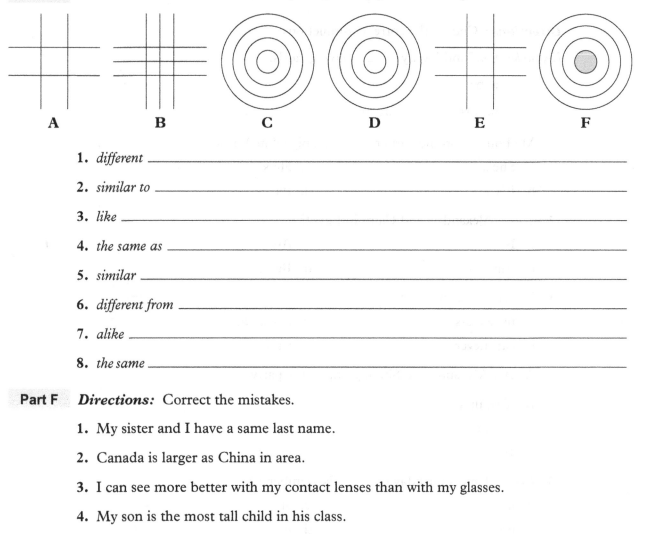

A   B   C   D   E   F

1. *different* _____

2. *similar to* _____

3. *like* _____

4. *the same as* _____

5. *similar* _____

6. *different from* _____

7. *alike* _____

8. *the same* _____

Part F *Directions:* Correct the mistakes.

1. My sister and I have a same last name.

2. Canada is larger as China in area.

3. I can see more better with my contact lenses than with my glasses.

4. My son is the most tall child in his class.

5. Men's basketball and women's basketball are like in many ways.

6. Yasuko's dictionary is different to mine.

7. My other book is interesting more than this one.

Directions: Choose the correct completions.

Example: Josef and Henry _____ playing cards.

      a. be   c. is

      b. was   ⓓ are

1. My house is on the corner. _____ a big white house.

    a. She's   c. He's

    b. It's   d. Its

2. _____ Alexandria and Cairo in Egypt?

    a. Is   c. Are

    b. Am   d. Be

3. Nader _____ breakfast.

    a. never eats   c. never eat

    b. eats never   d. eat never

4. A: Are Mr. and Mrs. Shinn going to the party?

    B: Yes, they _____ .

        a. do   c. are

        b. go   d. going

5. My husband's birthday is _____ November 12.

    a. in   c. at

    b. on   d. to

6. Mrs. Wheeler has two cats. _____ names are Suzy and Max.

    a. They   c. They're

    b. Its   d. Their

7. Song is _____ honor student at the University of Texas.

    a. a   c. some

    b. an   d. the

8. I _____ my phone ringing, but I can't find it!

    a. am hearing   c. am listening

    b. hear   d. listen to

9. Javier plays soccer three times a week. He _____ plays soccer.

    a. never   c. often

    b. seldom   d. always

10. My mother _____ a nap right now. She can't talk on the phone.

a. take

c. takes

b. is taking

d. taking

11. Billy usually gets home from school _____ 4:00.

a. to

c. at

b. on

d. in

12. I'm looking for some good _____ books.

a. children's

c. childrens

b. childs

d. children

13. A: Is Mr. Jamieson in his office?

B: _____

a. Yes, it is.

c. No, he doesn't.

b. Yes, he is.

d. No, he not.

14. We need _____ new furniture for our living room.

a. a

c. some

b. an

d. many

15. A: _____ is the nearest drugstore?

B: It's on Jefferson Street.

a. Who

c. What

b. Where

d. That

16. My little brother eats all the time. He _____ hungry.

a. always is

c. eats

b. always

d. is always

17. I _____ using my laptop to do my homework.

a. be

c. is

b. am

d. are

18. Jared _____ electric cars are great because they don't use gasoline.

a. is thinking about

c. thinks that

b. think that

d. thinks about

19. Susan works Saturdays _____ 7:00 A.M. to 5:00 P.M.

a. at

c. in

b. on

d. from

20. A: Does Mrs. Al-Rafie often work late?

B: Yes, _____ does.

a. she

c. her

b. he

d. him

21. I usually eat _____ soup for lunch.

    a. a

    b. a bar of

    c. a bowl of

    d. a bottle of

22. A: _____ those men?

    B: Sorry. I don't know them.

       a. Who are

       b. Who is

       c. Whose

       d. Who's

23. Sami _____ this assignment by tomorrow.

    a. need to finishes

    b. need to finish

    c. needs to finish

    d. needs to finishes

24. Michel and Victor _____ studying at the library. They're at home.

    a. don't

    b. isn't

    c. aren't

    d. not

25. Valentine's Day is _____ February.

    a. in

    b. on

    c. from

    d. at

26. We always have to solve _____ in Calculus.

    a. problems difficults

    b. problems difficult

    c. difficults problems

    d. difficult problems

27. A: Where _____ ?

    B: At the pharmacy.

       a. do Ben work

       b. is Ben work

       c. Ben works

       d. does Ben work

28. My sister and _____ like to watch movies together.

    a. I

    b. me

    c. my

    d. myself

29. Our teacher doesn't have _____ information about the new club.

    a. some

    b. an

    c. many

    d. much

30. _____ you a doctor?

    a. Is

    b. Are

    c. Am

    d. What

31. My dad takes the train to work. He _____.

    a. not drive

    b. don't drive

    c. doesn't drive

    d. isn't driving

32. A: Why _____ ?

B: Because the baby is sleeping.

    a. do you whisper   c. are you whispering

    b. you are whispering   d. you whisper

33. There _____ seven students in Hanna's class.

    a. is   c. has

    b. are   d. have

34. A: _____ is that?

B: It's Jay's.

    a. Whose dog   c. Whose dogs

    b. Who's dog   d. Who's dogs

35. I only have _____ homework tonight.

    a. a few   c. any

    b. a little   d. many

36. Cathy enjoys watching _____ basketball.

    a. women   c. womens'

    b. womens   d. women's

37. Anna isn't a teacher. _____ an accountant.

    a. She   c. She's

    b. Is   d. Shes

38. _____ her dogs twice a day?

    a. Does Nancy feed   c. Do Nancy feed

    b. Does Nancy feeds   d. Is Nancy feeds

39. A: How many theaters _____ in New York City?

B: At least 80.

    a. there are   c. is there

    b. there is   d. are there

40. My parents gave _____ some money for my birthday.

    a. I   c. my

    b. me   d. myself

41. Nalawer has four _____, two girls and two boys.

    a. child   c. children

    b. childs   d. childrens

42. A: James, can you reach _____ book on the top shelf?

B: Sure. Here it is.

    a. the   c. an

    b. a   d. Ø

43. I'm too busy today! I don't have _____ time for lunch.

    a. some   c. a

    b. any   d. an

44. My brother has a new car. _____ car is red.

    a. Her   c. It

    b. My   d. His

45. A: Do you like horror films?

B: No, _____.

    a. you don't   c. I don't

    b. you're not   d. I'm not

46. I am listening to a song, but I _____ the words.

    a. don't understand   c. no understand

    b. am not understand   d. don't understanding

47. _____ something to eat now?

    a. Do you like   c. You like

    b. Would you like   d. Are you like

48. Can I borrow _____ eraser? I can't find mine.

    a. you   c. yours

    b. your   d. you're

49. Right now, I _____ our last vacation. We had a wonderful time at the beach.

    a. think that   c. am thinking that

    b. think about   d. am thinking about

50. It's a beautiful day! _____ sun is shining!

    a. A   c. The

    b. An   d. Ø

Part A *Directions:* Complete the sentences with the correct form of the words in parentheses. Use the simple present or the present progressive.

Example: My aunt (*come*) _____comes_____ to visit us on weekends.

1. Suzy (*have, often*) _____ tests at school. She (*study*) _____ hard. Right now, she (*take*) _____ an English test.

2. In the summer, I (*have, usually*) _____ ice cream for dessert. It (*taste*) _____ cold and delicious. In the winter, I (*eat, not*) _____ ice cream.

3. My friends (*think*) _____ about going to the beach this afternoon. Sam (*want*) _____ to go to Marina Beach. Mika (*think*) _____ that Sunset Beach is nice.

4. Today the weather (*be*) _____ perfect! The sun (*shine*) _____, and it (*be, not*) _____ too hot.

5. Right now, Pippa (*wear*) _____ her new black boots. They (*look*) _____ nice, but Pippa's feet (*hurt*) _____.

Part B *Directions:* Make yes/no questions. Give short answers. Use the simple present or the present progressive.

Example: A: _____Do you usually eat breakfast_____?

B: _____No, I don't_____. (I don't usually eat breakfast.)

1. A: _____?
   B: _____. (*Wendy teaches music.*)

2. A: _____?
   B: _____. (*I am not watching a movie now.*)

3. A: _____?
   B: _____. (*The girls play soccer every Saturday.*)

4. A: _____?
   B: _____. (*The workers at Country Market are usually helpful.*)

5. A: _____?
   B: _____. (*Paulo is studying at the library.*)

Part C *Directions:* Make information questions. Use the simple present or the present progressive.

Example: A: _____ *What do you usually wear to school* _____ ?

   B: A uniform. (*I usually wear a uniform to school.*)

1. A: _____ ?

   B: In Miami. (*Marta lives in Miami.*)

2. A: _____ ?

   B: A salad. (*I'm making a salad.*)

3. A: _____ ?

   B: Thirty-five. (*There are thirty-five students in my French class.*)

4. A: _____ ?

   B: Because it's fun. (*Cecilia is learning to dance because it's fun.*)

5. A: _____ ?

   B: It's rainy and cold. (*The weather is rainy and cold today.*)

Part D *Directions:* Circle the correct completions.

Example: I work ((*in*,) *on, at*) downtown Seattle.

SITUATION: *My Job*

1. I work in (*a, an, the*) office building. It is (*on, in, at*) Seneca Street.

2. I usually start work (*on, from, at*) 8:30 A.M. I work (*on, from, at*) 8:30 A.M. to 4:30 P.M.

3. (*There is, There are*) a lot of work to do every day. I have (*much, many*) things to do.

4. Mr. Robbins is (*me, my, mine*) boss. (*He, His, Him*) is a very nice man.

5. Today we have (*a, an, the*) big meeting. (*A, Some, The*) businessmen from Osaka are here.

Part E *Directions:* Complete the sentences with **much** or **many** and the correct form of the noun in *italics*. Use the plural where needed.

Example: money   My brother doesn't have _____ *much money* _____ .

        book   We have too _____ *many books* _____ to carry.

1. *tomato*   We always plant _____ in our garden.

2. *coffee*   I don't drink _____ . I like tea better.

3. *homework*   How _____ do you have tonight?

4. *friend*   Marisa is a friendly person. She has _____ .

5. *child*   _____ ride their bicycles to school.

Part F *Directions:* Correct the mistakes.

music

Example: Jerry listens to a lot of ~~musics.~~

1. I have a information about the driving test.

2. My mother needs to get a bag of olive oil at the store.

3. Who's book is this?

4. I don't have some paper. Can I borrow some?

5. There's too much traffics in the city.

6. Our teacher gave us a little problems to do for homework.

7. My dad is eating breakfast in a kitchen.

8. Yours coffee has sugar in it.

9. Joao has problems with his tooths. He has to go to the dentist.

10. Pats car keys are in his coat pocket.

Directions: Choose the correct completions.

Example: My birthday is _____ September 8.

    a. in   c. at

    (b.) on   d. from

1. My brother and I play basketball after school. _____ love basketball.

    a. They   c. We

    b. He   d. Us

2. Miss Crawley _____ a good job in London.

    a. have   c. is having

    b. haves   d. has

3. _____ today?

    a. Does it rain   c. Is it raining

    b. Rains it   d. It rains

4. Mr. Easton _____ water at lunch.

    a. often drinks   c. drink often

    b. often drink   d. drinks often

5. I bought _____ meat at the grocery store.

    a. a   c. some

    b. many   d. a few

6. My parents usually don't go out _____ night.

    a. in   c. on

    b. at   d. in the

7. _____ doctors worked to save the man's life.

    a. A   c. One

    b. An   d. Ø

8. A: Where _____ you last night?

    B: At my exercise class.

        a. was   c. are

        b. were   d. did

9. After Simone tried on the shoes, she _____.

    a. bought them   c. pays for them

    b. wore it   d. went to the shoe store

10. Next Saturday we _____ movies at my friend's house.

   a. watch

   b. watched

   c. were watching

   d. are going to watch

11. I'm hot and have a headache. I _____ sick.

   a. maybe

   b. might be

   c. will be

   d. may not be

12. If Joe _____ the bus, he'll be late for work today.

   a. will miss

   b. miss

   c. misses

   d. am going to miss

13. Rina speaks Japanese fluently. She _____ speak English well.

   a. cans

   b. doesn't know

   c. can't

   d. not able to

14. Mari made a _____ for dinner.

   a. fruit salad delicious

   b. fruit delicious salad

   c. delicious fruits salad

   d. delicious fruit salad

15. Jan and her sister are twins. They look _____.

   a. alike

   b. like

   c. similar to

   d. the same as

16. My aunt is a doctor. _____ a nurse.

   a. She not

   b. She isn't

   c. She aren't

   d. She's no

17. David and Ray are wearing jackets. _____ jackets are new.

   a. Their

   b. They

   c. They're

   d. Them

18. William _____ playing the guitar.

   a. enjoy

   b. enjoies

   c. enjoys

   d. enjoying

19. Right now, we _____ for a taxi.

   a. wait

   b. are waiting

   c. waiting

   d. do wait

20. How many parks _____ in this city?

   a. are there

   b. is there

   c. there are

   d. there is

21. My friend has two white _____.

   a. mouse   c. mice

   b. mouses   d. mouse's

22. Would you like _____ strawberries?

   a. some   c. much

   b. an   d. a little

23. A: Where's Mom?

   B: She's in _____ kitchen.

      a. a   c. the

      b. an   d. Ø

24. Tony played soccer with his friends _____ afternoon.

   a. yesterday   c. ago

   b. last   d. at

25. A: Who _____ at the café last Saturday?

   B: I met Bev and Sara.

      a. did you met   c. you met

      b. do you meet   d. did you meet

26. When I woke up at 3:00 A.M., _____.

   a. I am tired   c. my baby is crying

   b. I hear the baby   d. my baby was crying

27. It's 7:00 A.M. Elizabeth _____ to school this morning at 8:00 A.M.

   a. goes   c. is going to go

   b. went   d. was going

28. Lily can't drink this tea. It's _____ hot.

   a. very   c. much

   b. too   d. many

29. My little sister learns languages more _____ than me.

   a. easier   c. easiest

   b. easily   d. easy

30. _____ you and Becky classmates?

   a. Do   c. Is

   b. Does   d. Are

31. That test was _____ test of the entire semester.

   a. more difficult   c. most difficult

   b. difficulter   d. the most difficult

32. I like _____ jewelry.

    a. this

    b. a

    c. these

    d. those

33. A: _____ does your sister work?

    B: At Beatty's Bookstore.

    a. Who

    b. What

    c. Where

    d. Why

34. My son really _____ his teacher this year.

    a. like

    b. is liking

    c. likes

    d. alike

35. Alicia's grandparents live in a different town. She wants to visit _____.

    a. they

    b. their

    c. them

    d. they're

36. You need _____ umbrella when you live in Seattle.

    a. a

    b. an

    c. the

    d. Ø

37. A: _____ his bicycle to work yesterday?

    B: No. He took the bus.

    a. Did Jim ride

    b. Jim rode

    c. Was Jim ride

    d. Rode Jim

38. While we _____, Roger came into the computer lab.

    a. talking

    b. was talking

    c. were talking

    d. are talking

39. A: Will Ahmed go bowling this weekend?

    B: No, _____.

    a. he will

    b. he's not

    c. he isn't

    d. he won't

40. What _____ next weekend?

    a. did you do

    b. you may do

    c. you are going to do

    d. are you going to do

41. A: What's wrong?

    B: I need help with grammar. I _____ understand this sentence.

    a. won't

    b. could

    c. can't

    d. couldn't

42. People _____ drive so fast. It's dangerous.

    a. shouldn't   c. could

    b. should   d. couldn't

43. A: Are you hungry?

    B: Yes. I would like _____ to eat, please.

        a. anybody   c. someone

        b. anything   d. something

44. Most of the texts on my phone _____ from my best friend.

    a. are   c. is

    b. they're   d. it's

45. Stan likes to watch sports on TV, but his wife _____.

    a. isn't   c. doesn't

    b. aren't   d. don't

46. A: Is your first name Chen?

    B: Yes, _____.

        a. I am   c. I do

        b. it is   d. it does

47. _____ that man?

    a. Whose   c. Who's

    b. Who are   d. What are

48. I don't need _____ help with my homework.

    a. a   c. some

    b. an   d. any

49. Mr. Porter _____ his laptop computer to work.

    a. brang   c. bringed

    b. brought   d. braught

50. Chris _____ home from Europe next summer.

    a. come   c. is going to come

    b. came   d. was coming

Part A **Directions:** Complete the sentences with the correct form of the verbs in parentheses. Use the simple present, simple past, or future.

Example: She (*want*) _____wants_____ to be an actress.

SITUATION: *Anne Hathaway's Life—1982–present*

1. Anne Hathaway (*be*) _____ an American actress. Many people around the world (*enjoy*) _____ her performances.

2. Anne (*grow*) _____ up in Brooklyn, New York, and (*start*) _____ acting at a young age.

3. In 2001, Anne (*become*) _____ famous in the movie *The Princess Diaries*.

4. In 2008, Anne (*get*) _____ some awards for her part in *Rachel Getting Married*.

5. In 2013, she (*win*) _____ an Academy Award for playing Fantine in *Les Miserables*.

6. In the next few years, Anne Hathaway (*star*) _____ in other films. I (*watch*) _____ all of them.

7. I (*like*) _____ Anne Hathaway's work very much.

Part B **Directions:** Complete the sentences with the correct form of the verbs in parentheses. Use the simple present, the present progressive, the simple past, or the past progressive.

Example: Jim usually (*have*) _____has_____ cereal for breakfast, but today he (*eat*) _____is eating_____ eggs.

1. Right now, I (*take*) _____ a test. I always (*feel*) _____ nervous about tests.

2. Last year, Mr. and Mrs. Winston (*go*) _____ to Greece on their vacation. While they (*travel*) _____, they (*meet*) _____ many nice people.

3. Yesterday when my mother (*send*) _____ me a text, I (*drive*) _____, so I couldn't answer it.

4. Marcos (*get*) _____ a lot of email every day. He usually (*use*) _____ his laptop to check the email, but right now he (*check*) _____ his email on his phone.

Part C   *Directions:* Make yes/no questions. Give short answers.

Example: A: _____ *Do you usually eat breakfast* _____ ?

B: _____ *No, I don't* _____ . (*I don't usually eat breakfast.*)

1. A: _____ ?

B: _____ . (*Maiko and Anton are sitting in the front row.*)

2. A: _____ ?

B: _____ . (*I didn't go to the supermarket last Saturday.*)

3. A: _____ ?

B: _____ . (*Fatima will make fish and rice for dinner.*)

4. A: _____ ?

B: _____ . (*My car doesn't use much gas.*)

5. A: _____ ?

B: _____ . (*Jim was planning to go to the party.*)

Part D   *Directions:* Make information questions.

Example: A: _____ *What do you usually wear to school* _____ ?

B: A uniform. (*I usually wear a uniform to school.*)

1. A: _____ ?

B: Ancient Greece. (*The program was about Ancient Greece.*)

2. A: _____ ?

B: Next summer. (*Pat and Andrea are going to go to Yellowstone Park next summer.*)

3. A: _____ ?

B: Went to a movie. (*We went to a movie last night.*)

4. A: _____ ?

B: In the garage. (*Your tennis racket is in the garage.*)

5. A: _____ ?

B: Because he needed some cash. (*Kevin went to the bank because he needed some cash.*)

Part E **Directions:** Choose the correct completions.

Example: My mother is a photographer. (She, Her) likes her job.

1. I don't have (*any, some*) money. I spent it on (*my, mine*) lunch.

2. That is Tom's house. The one next to it is (*our, ours*).

3. That author wrote three (*book, books*). The (*book's, books'*) titles are different, but they are all mysteries.

4. I'd like (*a, the*) ham sandwich, please.

5. Josh read (*a, an*) interesting story about life in (*a, the*) future.

6. (*Willy's, Willy*) roommate listens to (*a few, a little*) music every day.

7. Carol and Tony ate some delicious (*vegetables, vegetable*) soup for dinner.

8. The men worked (*quick, quickly*) to finish the roof.

9. Everyone (*use, uses*) the Internet to find (*an, Ø*) information.

10. Sohib didn't buy (*nothing, anything*) at the department store.

Part F **Directions:** Correct the mistakes.

Example: A fish ~~can~~ use a computer. *can't*

1. Our basketball team maybe win the game tomorrow.

2. Can Trent speaks Spanish well?

3. The movie was too funny. I enjoyed it.

4. Children shouldn't get 8-10 hours of sleep every night. It's healthy.

5. Clara have to take her driver's test next Friday.

6. Mr. Paxton must not work any more. He is retired.

7. Please to finish your homework before you go out.

8. Fred is handsomer than his friend.

9. My dog is the cuter dog in the world.

10. Max and Mark are classmates. They have same teacher.

ANSWER KEY

CHAPTER 1

Quiz 1, p. 1

1. she
2. it
3. he
4. she
5. it
6. he
7. it
8. she
9. he
10. it

Quiz 2, p. 1

1. He is
2. are
3. He is
4. It is
5. am
6. It is
7. She is
8. are
9. am
10. It is

Quiz 3, p. 2

A.
2. you
3. we
4. you
5. they
6. we

B.
2. We
3. They
4. They
5. We
6. You

Quiz 4, p. 2

1. am
2. are
3. is
4. are
5. is
6. are
7. is
8. is
9. is
10. are

Quiz 5, p. 3

2. an
3. a
4. an
5. a
6. a
7. a
8. a
9. an
10. a
11. an

Quiz 6, p. 3

2. a language
3. a country
4. a book
5. a city
6. a sport
7. an animal
8. a street
9. a girl
10. a color
11. an island

Quiz 7, p. 4

1. Cats are animals.
2. Roses are flowers.
3. Hotels are buildings.
4. Computers are machines.
5. Dictionaries are books.
6. London and Chicago are cities.
7. French and Arabic are languages.
8. Tennis and baseball are sports.
9. Dyanne and Fatima are teachers.
10. Summer and winter are seasons.

Quiz 8, p. 5

1. You are beautiful.
2. Spring is a season.
3. A rose is a flower.
4. We are hungry.
5. A bird is an animal.
6. They are funny.
7. I am a singer.
8. Egypt and Italy are countries.
9. You are students.
10. Carrots are vegetables.

Quiz 9, p. 5

1. I'm
2. He's
3. She's
4. We're
5. They're
6. She's
7. He's
8. They're
9. It's
10. You're

Quiz 10, p. 6

1. is, isn't
2. are, aren't
3. isn't, is
4. are, aren't
5. aren't, are

Quiz 11, p. 6

1. (They)'re not, aren't
2. (He)'s not, isn't
3. (She)'s not, isn't
4. (We)'re not, aren't
5. (You)'re not, aren't
6. (I)'m not

Quiz 12, p. 7

2. dirty
3. unfriendly
4. dangerous
5. beautiful
6. quiet
7. uncrowded
8. cold
9. warm
10. cheap
11. dry
12. happy
13. sour
14. poor
15. tall
16. sick

Quiz 13, p. 8

2. sweet, (They)'re sour
3. dirty, (It)'s clean
4. rich, (She)'s poor
5. fast, (They)'re slow
6. hot, (He)'s cold
7. wet, (They)'re dry
8. new, (It)'s old
9. happy, (She)'s sad
10. short, (He)'s tall
11. dangerous, (It)'s safe

Quiz 14, p. 8

1. Lemons aren't red. They're yellow.
2. English isn't easy. It's difficult.
3. Balls aren't square. They're round.
4. A pen isn't heavy. It's light.
5. A mouse isn't big. It's little.

Quiz 15, p. 9

2. under
3. next to
4. in
5. on
6. behind
7. next to
8. between
9. in

Quiz 16, p. 10

2. Lina, is, noun
3. He, is, place
4. They, are, place
5. Dan, is, noun
6. You, are, adjective
7. Maya, is, place
8. We, are, adjective
9. They, are, noun
10. My books, are, place
11. I, am, adjective

Quiz 17, p. 10

2. Nina and Maria are
3. Many students are OR My brother is
4. My brother is OR Many students are
5. Oranges are
6. Basketball is
7. Carrots are
8. Beijing is
9. Peru and Ecuador are
10. Spanish is
11. Computer games are

TEST 1, p. 11

A.
1. Onions are vegetables.
2. Birds are animals.
3. Lemons are yellow.
4. Jakarta and Seoul are cities.
5. Tennis and soccer are sports.

B.
1. It's
2. She's
3. They're
4. He's
5. I'm

C.
1. is not OR isn't
2. are not OR aren't
3. am not OR (I)'m not
4. is not OR isn't
5. are not OR aren't

D.
1. Cars aren't cheap. They are expensive.
2. A rose isn't ugly. It is beautiful.
3. Lemons aren't sweet. They are sour.
4. Grammar isn't difficult/easy. It is easy/difficult.
   Grammar is difficult/easy. It isn't easy/difficult.
5. Jonas isn't an adult/a child. He is a child/an adult.
   Jonas is an adult/a child. He isn't a child/an adult.

E.
1. under
2. on
3. in
4. above
5. next to

TEST 2, p. 13

A.
1. Dictionaries are books.
2. Balls are round.
3. Airplanes are fast.
4. Chinese and Japanese are languages.
5. Cuba and Turkey are countries.

B.
1. It's
2. We're
3. It's
4. He's
5. They're

C.
1. is not OR isn't
2. are not OR aren't
3. are not OR aren't
4. is not OR isn't
5. am not OR (I)'m not

D.
1. A box isn't round. It is square.
2. The sun is hot. It isn't cold.
3. Bananas aren't blue. They are yellow.
4. Rain forests are wet. They aren't dry.
5. A coin isn't large. It is small.

E.
1. in
2. above
3. between
4. under
5. on

CHAPTER 2

Quiz 1, p. 15

A.
1. Are
2. Are
3. Is
4. Am
5. Are

B.
1. Is David from Toronto?
2. Are cows animals?
3. Are Paulo and Marie in the library?
4. Is the weather cold today?
5. Am I a student? OR Are you a student?

Quiz 2, p. 16

1. A: Are you homesick?
   B: Yes, I am.
2. A: Is Katya a nurse?
   B: Yes, she is.
3. A: Are you and Gina roommates?
   B: Yes, we are.
4. A: Is Rico married?
   B: No, he isn't.
5. A: Are your grandparents in Mexico?
   B: No, they aren't.

6. A: Are you a doctor?
   B: No, I'm not.
7. A: Is Mr. Kimura in his office?
   B: Yes, he is.
8. A: Are you tired?
   B: No, we're not.
9. A: Are cars expensive?
   B: Yes, they are.
10. A: Is Julia in the apartment?
    B: No, she isn't.

Quiz 3, p. 17

1. Is Carmen in New York this week?
   Where is Carmen?
2. Where are Yoko and Rita now?
   Are Yoko and Rita at the zoo?
3. Is Mr. Morsten at work today?
   Where is Mr. Morsten?
4. Where is the train station?
   Is the train station on Railroad Avenue?
5. Are my/your sunglasses in the car?
   Where are my/your sunglasses?

Quiz 4, p. 18

1. has
2. have
3. has
4. have
5. have
6. has
7. have
8. have
9. has, has

Quiz 5, p. 18

1. has, are
2. have, is
3. is, has
4. have, are
5. are, have

Quiz 6, p. 19

1. Her
2. Their
3. Our
4. His
5. Their
6. Your
7. Our
8. Your
9. My
10. Their

Quiz 7, p. 19

1. have, Your
2. has, His
3. have, Their
4. have, My
5. have, Your
6. has, Her
7. have, Our
8. have, Their
9. has, His
10. has, Her

Quiz 8, p. 20

2. That
3. That
4. This
5. This
6. That

Quiz 9, p. 20

2. These
3. Those
4. Those
5. These
6. Those

Quiz 10, p. 21

2. These, That
3. That, This
4. Those, These
5. This, That
6. That, These

Quiz 11, p. 21

1. Who are
2. What is
3. What are
4. Who is
5. What is
6. What are
7. What is
8. Who are
9. What is
10. Who is

Quiz 12, p. 22

2. a
3. b
4. b
5. c
6. b
7. c
8. b
9. a
10. c
11. c
12. b
13. c
14. a
15. c
16. b

Quiz 13, p. 23

2. **These / Those** earrings are beautiful.
3. My father is **a** gardener.
4. **What is / What's** your name?
5. My sister **has** two children.
6. Natalie **is not / isn't** at school today.
7. **Is Ms. Rossi** your teacher?
8. I have **an** apple in my backpack.
9. You have a notebook. **Your** notebook is yellow.
10. Roberto and Will are students in my class. They are **intelligent**.
11. This **isn't** my raincoat.
12. **Who is / Who's** your favorite teacher?
13. **That ring is** expensive. / **Those rings are** expensive.
14. **Are** the children sick?
15. Michael **has** three cats.
16. You and your brother **are** students.

TEST 1, p. 24

A.

1. A: Are you a student?
   B: Yes, I am.
2. A: Is Selma in your class?
   B: No, she isn't./No, she's not.
3. A: Are your classmates friendly?
   B: Yes, they are.
4. A: Is that book interesting?
   B: Yes, it is.
5. A: Are Marcos and David doctors?
   B: No, they aren't./No, they're not.

B.

1. has, His
2. have, Our
3. has, Her
4. have, Their
5. have, My

C.

1. This, Those
2. Those, These
3. Those, This
4. This, This
5. That, Those

D.
1. c
2. a
3. d
4. c
5. b

E.
1. Our teacher **isn't** at school today. She **has** the flu.
2. You have a fever. **Your** head is hot.
3. Where **is** Roberto? **Is he** at school?
4. My book **is** not in my backpack. **Where is** my book?
5. A: Are you homesick?
   B: Yes, **I am.**

TEST 2, p. 26

A.
1. A: Is Mrs. Ramirez sick?
   B: Yes, she is.
2. A: Is Joe from London?
   B: No, he isn't.
3. A: Are those shoes comfortable?
   B: Yes, they are.
4. A: Is Quebec in the United States?
   B: No, it isn't.
5. A: Are you and your sister in the same class?
   B: Yes, we are.

B.
1. have, My
2. have, Our
3. have, Your
4. has, Her
5. have, Their

C.
1. That, These
2. This, That
3. Those, This
4. These, These
5. Those, These

D.
1. b
2. d
3. c
4. c
5. a

E.
1. Mr. Chang **has** a blue jacket.
2. **Who is** your English teacher?
3. Carlos and Maria **have** a house in Mexico. **Their** house is beautiful.
4. **These/Those** are your sunglasses. They **aren't** my sunglasses.
5. **Where is** your apartment? **Is it** on Grand Street?

CHAPTER 3

Quiz 1, p. 28
1. like
2. likes
3. like
4. like
5. likes
6. like
7. likes
8. like
9. likes
10. like

Quiz 2, p. 28
1. does
2. eat
3. watch
4. walks
5. begins
6. go
7. eat
8. studies
9. talk
10. walk

Quiz 3, p. 29

A.
2. always
3. usually
4. never
5. sometimes
6. seldom/rarely

B.
1. sometimes
2. seldom
3. never
4. often
5. always

Quiz 4, p. 30

A.
1. once a year
2. three times a day
3. twice a month
4. four times a week
5. six times a day

B.
1. Marcos is usually in the cafeteria at 12:00.
2. Gloria sometimes stays at school in the afternoon.
3. I am often at home by three o'clock.
4. My sisters are always at home in the evening.
5. They never go to bed late.

Quiz 5, p. 31
2. sits
3. pushes
4. kisses
5. takes
6. fixes
7. watches
8. speaks
9. talks
10. brushes
11. teaches

Quiz 6, p. 32
2. flies
3. tries
4. buys
5. studies
6. enjoys
7. stays
8. pays
9. plays
10. says
11. cries

Quiz 7, p. 33
1. goes
2. does
3. go
4. have
5. do
6. has
7. goes
8. has
9. do
10. goes

Quiz 8, p. 33
1. never worries
2. often invites
3. usually spend
4. has
5. sometimes plays
6. often surf
7. is always
8. goes
9. usually watch
10. say

Quiz 9, p. 34

A.
1. Natalie needs to buy vegetables.
2. I want to go to the library.
3. My dad likes to read on the Internet.
4. Felix and you need to study.
5. Dr. Swanson likes to help people.

B.
1. I **need** to find my keys.
2. Francisco **wants** to watch the news on TV.
3. Sam likes to **answer** questions in class.
4. Anna needs **to** help her mother today.
5. My brother and I **like** to eat ice cream.

Quiz 10, p. 34

1. doesn't take
2. don't know
3. don't live
4. doesn't want
5. don't drive
6. don't like
7. doesn't work
8. doesn't study
9. doesn't have
10. don't do

Quiz 11, p. 35

1. does not
2. do not
3. are not
4. does not
5. is not
6. do not
7. does not
8. am not
9. does not
10. do not

Quiz 12, p. 35

1. often comes
2. don't have, has, washes, never washes, don't like
3. don't have, don't need
4. plays, doesn't do

Quiz 13, p. 36

A.
1. b
2. a
3. a
4. b
5. b

B.
1. **Do** Petra and Ivan need help?
2. Do you **do** your homework every day?
3. Does he **speak** Japanese?
4. **Do they like** Chinese food? OR **Do I like** Chinese food?
5. **Does Katya** take a nap in the afternoon?

Quiz 14, p. 37

1. Do you play . . . ? . . . I do.
2. Is Maria . . . ? . . . she isn't.
3. Does Rob have . . . ? . . . he doesn't.
4. Do Paulo and Lana live . . . ? . . . they do.
5. Does it snow . . . ? . . . it does.
6. Is it . . . ? . . . it isn't.
7. Do you/we have . . . ? . . . I/we don't.
8. Does Amanda wear . . . ? . . . she doesn't.
9. Are they . . . ? . . . they are.
10. Do your friends walk . . . ? . . . they don't.

Quiz 15, p. 38

1. Where do you live?
2. What does Bonnie like?
3. What do they need?
4. Where does Vinesh often go?
5. What does Jared teach?
6. Where does Angela buy vegetables?
7. What do Makda and Delina want?
8. Where does Artur work?
9. Where do you always put flowers?
10. What does Todd usually eat for lunch?

Quiz 16, p. 39

1. Where do you play basketball?
2. What time/When do the girls go to bed?
3. What does Waleed want?
4. What time/When does the restaurant close?
5. What do they study?
6. Where does he hang his coat?
7. What time/When does Karl usually do his homework?
8. Where does Tara often study?
9. What time/When do you usually cook dinner?
10. What time/When does Lisa usually go home?

Quiz 17, p. 40

1. c
2. b, c, a
3. b, a, b
4. a, c, b

Quiz 18, p. 41

1. is
2. do
3. Are
4. is
5. does
6. Is
7. Does
8. does
9. do
10. Do

Quiz 19, p. 41

2. We **always speak** English in class.
3. . . . My friend **studies** at the library.
4. B: Yes, I **do**.
5. **Does** your sister have a computer at home?
6. We **don't** need new clothes.
7. My roommate **doesn't** drink coffee.
8. . . . .She **has** a diamond ring.
9. Does Franco **play** soccer every weekend?
10. What time **do** you go to school?
11. Eli **doesn't** drive to school every morning.

TEST 1, p. 42

A.
1. speaks, speak
2. goes, go
3. buys, buys
4. study, studies
5. teach, teaches

B.
1. works, doesn't leave, rarely gets, is usually, doesn't have
2. stay, don't go, don't like, usually go, always have

C.
1. Marta **misses** her brothers. They **live** in Venezuela.
2. Quan doesn't **have** a car. He **usually takes** the bus.
3. What time **does** Teresa leave home every morning?
4. Ali **enjoys** soccer, but he **doesn't** like baseball.
5. I **don't** like pizza. **Do** you like pizza?

D.
1. b
2. a
3. b
4. b, a
5. c
6. a, a
7. b, b

TEST 2, p. 44

A.
1. works, work
2. has, have
3. catch, catches
4. carries, carries
5. play, plays

B.
1. is
2. live
3. live
4. doesn't live
5. lives
6. always writes
7. usually call
8. often talk
9. miss
10. misses

C.
1. Diane **talks** on her cell phone in her car. **I** never use my cell phone in my car.
2. What time **do** you go to bed every **night**?
3. Ingrid **doesn't** like school. She **often skips** class.
4. Mark **doesn't want** a new coat. He **doesn't need** a coat.
5. A: **Do** you know Jim Anderson?
   B: I'm not sure. Does he **have** blond hair?

D.
1. c
2. b
3. c
4. a
5. b, c
6. a, c
7. b, b

CHAPTER 4

Quiz 1, p. 46

1. is
2. are
3. am
4. are
5. is
6. are
7. is
8. are
9. are
10. am

Quiz 2, p. 46

2. fixing
3. sleeping
4. stopping
5. getting
6. driving
7. buying
8. counting
9. reading
10. brushing
11. putting
12. making
13. swimming
14. studying
15. smiling
16. playing

Quiz 3, p. 47

1. is shining
2. are walking
3. is fishing
4. are having
5. is sitting
6. are climbing
7. are playing
8. are swimming
9. am riding
10. is barking

Quiz 4, p. 48

1. isn't wearing, is wearing
2. aren't eating, are eating
3. (I)'m not drinking, am drinking
4. isn't walking, is riding
5. isn't flying, is sleeping
6. aren't cleaning, are watching
7. aren't surfing, are using
8. isn't sitting, is running
9. aren't paying, are sending
10. isn't buying, is driving

Quiz 5, p. 49

1. A: Is Max taking
   B: he is
2. A: Are Tito and Anna studying
   B: they aren't
3. A: Is Ms. Park working
   B: she isn't
4. A: Is it snowing
   B: it is
5. A: Are you writing
   B: I am

Quiz 6, p. 49

1. Where is Abdul studying?
2. Why is Kate wearing a raincoat?
3. What are you making?
4. Where is Rita standing?
5. Why are you eating ice cream?

Quiz 7, p. 50

1. A: Are Maria and Paulo taking a cooking class?
   B: they are
2. A: Are you eating
   B: I'm not
3. Where is Cinda watching TV?
4. A: Is Anna playing
   B: she is
5. A: Is the sun shining?
   B: it isn't
6. Why are they eating cake?
7. What is Evan reading?
8. A: Are you going
   B: we are
9. Why is Alex studying?
10. What is Sherry doing?

Quiz 8, p. 51

1. is sleeping, sleeps
2. A: is snowing
   B: Does it snow
3. A: sits, isn't sitting
   B: is talking
4. am getting, isn't raining, (I)'m/am not wearing

Quiz 9, p. 51

1. Do
2. Is
3. Do
4. Is
5. Is
6. Are
7. Do
8. Does
9. Is
10. Does

Quiz 10, p. 52

1. is, Is
2. Do
3. is, are
4. Does
5. are, are, Are
6. does
7. is, Am, Am
8. Do, Are

Quiz 11, p. 52

1. is talking, likes, thinks
2. needs, is buying
3. are speaking, knows, understands
4. is eating, want

Quiz 12, p. 53

A.
1. watches
2. see
3. looking at
4. listens to
5. hear

B.
2. a phone
3. friends
4. music
5. a map
6. a movie

Quiz 13, p. 54

1. is thinking about
2. think that
3. thinks about
4. is thinking about, thinks about
5. think that
6. are thinking about, think that
7. am thinking about, think that

Quiz 14, p. 54

1. are sitting, are waiting, usually talk, isn't talking, is thinking, likes, thinks
2. is relaxing, are having, loves

Quiz 15, p. 55

1. . . . . **I want** a pizza.
2. Rosita **isn't** reading right now. She's **writing** in her notebook.
3. You **do** your homework every day.
4. . . . . He's listening **to** music.
5. Is the sun **shining** now?
6. . . . . I **don't believe** it.
7. **What are** the girls doing right now?
8. Right now I **am watching** a football game on TV. I think that football is exciting.

Quiz 16, p. 56

2. c
3. a
4. c
5. b
6. c
7. a
8. b
9. a
10. b
11. c

TEST 1, p. 57

A.
1. (I)'m not talking, am reading
2. isn't crying, is laughing
3. are running, aren't riding
4. isn't raining, is snowing
5. aren't eating, are drinking

B.
1. go, play
2. isn't, is working, works, is, likes
3. wants, is shopping, is looking

C.
1. b, b
2. a, c
3. a, b
4. b, c
5. b, a

D.
1. . . . .You **don't need** your coat.
2. Pablo **isn't sleeping** right now. . . . .
3. . . . .She **is getting** ready for school.
4. . . . .**Do you know** her name?
5. My parents **are** taking a walk right now.

TEST 2, p. 59

A.
1. is washing, isn't brushing
2. aren't sitting, are enjoying
3. isn't sleeping, is cleaning
4. are relaxing, aren't studying
5. am writing, (I)'m not making

B.
1. wears, is wearing
2. is flying, am
3. are, are watching, is eating, eat
4. need, don't understand

C.
1. b, b
2. c, a
3. a, c
4. c, b
5. c
6. b

D.
1. Right now Alex **is** doing his homework. He's **studying** grammar.
2. **Are you thinking** about grammar right now?
3. Pedro **isn't sitting** in his seat.....
4. I **am looking** at the sky right now. I see black clouds.
5. . . . .The baby is **smiling**.

CHAPTER 5

Quiz 1, p. 61
1. What day is it?
2. What time is it?
3. What year is it?
4. What time is it?
5. What month is it?
6. What's the date?
7. What time is it?
8. What's the date?
9. What day is it?
10. What's the date?

Quiz 2, p. 62
Possible answers:
1. It's (10:00).
2. It's (July 2nd, 2014).
3. It's (Tuesday).
4. It's (July).
5. It's (2014).

Quiz 3, p. 62
1. a. in
   b. on
   c. on
2. a. at
   b. on
3. a. in
   b. from, to
   c. in
   d. at

Quiz 4, p. 63
Answers for "B" may vary. Possible answers:
2. A. What's the weather like / How's the weather in Denver?
   B. It's chilly and sunny.
3. A. What's the weather like / How's the weather in Honolulu?
   B. It's cool and cloudy.
4. A. What's the weather like / How's the weather in Seattle?
   B. It's cold and stormy.
5. A. What's the weather like / How's the weather in Los Angeles?
   B. It's warm and clear.
6. A. What's the weather like / How's the weather in Chicago?
   B. It's below freezing and windy.

Quiz 5, p. 64
1. are
2. are
3. are
4. is
5. is
6. are
7. are
8. are
9. is
10. are

Quiz 6, p. 64
1. A: Are there any bears
   B: there are
2. A: Is there a cow
   B: there isn't
3. A: Is there a tiger
   B: there is
4. A: Are there any dogs
   B: there aren't
5. A: Is there a restaurant
   B: there is

Quiz 7, p. 65
A.
1. How many states are there in Mexico?
2. How many national holidays are there in Japan?
3. How many professional baseball teams are there in the USA?
4. How many minutes are there in a day?
5. How many national languages are there in Switzerland?

B.
Some answers will vary. Possible answers:
1. There are (12) people in this room.
2. There are 24 hours in a day.
3. There are 10 questions on this quiz.
4. There are 7 days in a week.
5. There are (2) children in my family.

Quiz 8, p. 66
A.
1. at
2. on, in, at
3. in

B.
2. in front of
3. in the back of
4. in back of
5. around, far away from

Quiz 9, p. 67
1. We would like / We'd like
2. A: Would you like to come
   B: I would like / I'd like to go
3. Liz would like / Liz'd like to have
4. She would like / She'd like
5. Tarek and Sam would like / Tarek and Sam'd like to eat
6. They would like / They'd like
7. A: Would Ruth like
   B: she would
8. We would like / We'd like to pay

Quiz 10, p. 68
1. A: like
   B: Would you like
   A: don't like, (I)'d like
2. A: Do you like
   B: like
   A: Would you like
   B: don't like, like, Would you like

Quiz 11, p. 68
1. are doing
2. is looking
3. understands
4. isn't writing
5. is thinking
6. thinks
7. doesn't want
8. to stop
9. needs
10. to finish

Quiz 12, p. 69
2. a
3. a, c
4. c
5. b
6. b
7. c
8. b
9. c, b

Quiz 13, p. 70

1. **There are** six eggs in the refrigerator.
2. Juanita **would** like a glass of water.
3. What time **is it?**
4. …She usually sits in **the** front of the bus.
5. …He **would like** to go to bed now.
6. Alexa's birthday is **on** August 19ᵗʰ.
7. How many big cities **are there** in China?
8. My parents live **on** Spring Street.
9. The bank isn't open **on** Sundays.
10. **What's the weather like** OR **How's the weather** in Seattle?

TEST 1, p. 71

A.
1. c, b
2. a
3. c
4. a, b
5. c, a
6. c
7. a

B.
1. There is
2. A: Are there
   B: there are
3. A: are there
   B: There are

C.
1. in
2. on
3. on
4. next to
5. between

D.
1. would like
2. likes
3. A: Would you like
   B: don't like
4. Do you like

E.
1. What **is/What's** the weather like in Athens?
2. Tomas **would** like a steak for dinner tonight.
3. How many countries **are there** in North America?
4. Please sit in **the** middle of the boat.
5. We live **at** 358 Norland Street.

TEST 2, p. 73

A.
1. b, a
2. c, b
3. a
4. b
5. a, c
6. a
7. c

B.
1. There is
2. A: Is there
   B: there isn't
3. A: are there
   B: There are

C.
1. on, at, in
2. on top of
3. behind

D.
1. would like
2. doesn't like
3. would you like
4. A: Would you like
   B: like

E.
1. **How is/How's** the weather in Montreal?
2. Marcos **would like** an ice cream cone.
3. How many days **are** there in June?
4. **There are** several good movies on TV tonight.
5. **I'd like/I would like** to watch TV now.

CHAPTER 6

Quiz 1, p. 75
Check 2, 5, 6, 8, 11

Quiz 2, p. 75
Check
3. I use my <u>cell phone</u> every day.
4. Sometimes I call <u>my friends</u>.
6. I send many <u>text messages</u> every day.
10. My cell phone takes <u>pictures</u> too.
11. I really like my <u>cell phone</u>.

Quiz 3, p. 76
1. a. My brother lives <u>in an apartment</u>.
   b. His apartment is <u>on the top floor</u>.
   c. He can see <u>across the city</u>.
2. a. Chang plays the violin <u>at school</u>.
   b. He sits <u>between Yun and Lian</u>.
   c. They often talk <u>during class</u>.
3. a. I am reading a story <u>about the future</u>.
   b. People travel <u>by spaceship</u>.
   c. There are people <u>from Mars</u>.
   d. There is a man <u>with three eyes</u>.

Quiz 4, p. 77

1.

The boys	play	games	in	the park
subject	verb	object of verb	preposition	object of prep.

2.

Ben and Lucia	have	a motorcycle	(none)	(none)
subject	verb	object of verb	preposition	object of prep.

3.

Alejandro	speaks	English and Spanish	(none)	(none)
subject	verb	object of verb	preposition	object of prep.

4.

The teacher	is drawing	a picture	on	the board
subject	verb	object of verb	preposition	object of prep.

5.

The students	are talking	(none)	about	their plans
subject	verb	object of verb	preposition	object of prep.

Quiz 5, p. 78

1. I sometimes put <u>fresh flowers</u> on my <u>desk</u>.
2. Mia needs a <u>strong backpack</u> for her <u>heavy books</u>.
3. My <u>lazy roommate</u> never changes his <u>dirty socks</u>.
4. Do your <u>friends</u> like <u>Vietnamese food</u>?
5. She'd like a <u>big cup</u> of <u>hot coffee</u> with <u>sugar</u>.
6. Do you want to read an <u>interesting story</u> about a <u>famous woman</u>?
7. <u>Students</u> often ask <u>difficult questions</u>.

8. (Evie) likes to wear black jeans.

9. A famous actress with beautiful hair stars in the movie.

10. Do you have exciting plans for your vacation?

Quiz 6, p. 78

1. me	6. it
2. you	7. us
3. them	8. you
4. her	9. them
5. him	10. it

Quiz 7, p. 79

1. I, them
2. she, She, it
3. us
4. her, We
5. me, I

Quiz 8, p. 80

2. thieves	7. parties
3. taxes	8. sandwiches
4. zoos	9. cowboys
5. knives	10. colleges
6. classmates	11. tomatoes

Quiz 9, p. 80

2. feet	7. teeth
3. fish	8. leaves
4. cities	9. sheep
5. men	10. women
6. mice	11. children

Quiz 10, p. 81

2. a	7. a
3. c	8. a
4. c	9. c
5. b	10. b
6. b	11. b

Quiz 11, p. 82

1. my, mine
2. your, yours
3. her, hers
4. his, his
5. our, ours
6. their, theirs

Quiz 12, p. 82

1. B: yours
   A: Mine, my, yours
2. B: hers, her
   A: his
3. B: their, yours
   A: Our

Quiz 13, p. 83

1. Andrea's	6. Sergei's
2. brothers'	7. friends'
3. mother's	8. teacher's
4. parents'	9. doctor's
5. boy's	10. Clay's

Quiz 14, p. 83

1. a. NC
   b. My aunt's name is Anna.
   c. My cousins' names are Susan and Elizabeth.
2. a. NC
   b. My grandparents' house is in the country.
   c. My mother's helping my grandmother.
3. a. NC
   b. My roommate's name is Matt.
   c. My roommate's studying engineering.
   d. ....Our friends' rooms are small.

Quiz 15, p. 84

A.

2. is that
3. is this
4. are these
5. are those
6. is this

B.

2. Whose
3. Who's
4. Whose
5. Whose
6. Who's

Quiz 16, p. 85

1. people's	6. woman's
2. women's	7. friends'
3. students'	8. person's
4. wife's	9. man's
5. men's	10. children's

Quiz 17, p. 85

1. **Whose** boots are these?
2. Rasheed **has** a new phone.
3. Do you like to go to **parties**?
4. How many **men** are there in your class?
5. My roommate and **I** have a big TV in our room.
6. My aunt has two little **children**.
7. **Who's** going to study for the test with you?
8. Those aren't **Mary's** glasses. Hers are in her purse.
9. There are two **languages** in Canada. People **speak** English and French.

TEST 1, p. 86

A.

1.

Karina	makes	breakfast	for	her children
subject	verb	object of verb	preposition	object of prep.

2.

Max and Mary	live	(none)	in	the country
subject	verb	object of verb	preposition	object of prep.

3.

I	like	sunny weather	(none)	(none)
subject	verb	object of verb	preposition	object of prep.

4.

The wind	is blowing	(none)	(none)	(none)
subject	verb	object of verb	preposition	object of prep.

B.
1. She
2. him
3. mine
4. It's
5. them

C.
1. cities
2. feet
3. children
4. wives
5. keys
6. dishes

D.
1. yours, Tony's, Your, His
2. Sarah's, Hers, the men's, their
3. doctor's, our

E.
1. Who's
2. Whose
3. Whose
4. Who's
5. Who's

F.
1. My friend is a **good dancer.**
2. Jorge and **I** play tennis every Saturday.
3. ... **My** dictionary is red.
4. There are two **zoos** in this city.
5. **Ladies** drink tea at the Empress Hotel.
6. Are these **your** keys?
7. **Women's** clothing is on the third floor.
8. My **wife's** sister works in a hospital.
9. Two of my **classmates** are planning a party.
10. **Who's** coming to the movie with us?

TEST 2, p. 88

A.
1.

We	visit	our grandparents	on	holidays
subject	verb	object of verb	preposition	object of prep.

2.

My cousins	live	(none)	in	France
subject	verb	object of verb	preposition	object of prep.

3.

The phone	is ringing	(none)	(none)	(none)
subject	verb	object of verb	preposition	object of prep.

4.

Gil	enjoys	the fresh air	in	the mountains.
subject	verb	object of verb	preposition	object of prep.

B.
1. him
2. my
3. them
4. I
5. their

C.
1. teeth
2. knives
3. dictionaries
4. days
5. glasses
6. tomatoes

D.
1. mine, yours, My, Your
2. Jake's, Their, Our
3. children's, Maya's, her

E.
1. Whose
2. Whose
3. Who's
4. Who's
5. Whose

F.
1. My grandmother **lives** in a small house.
2. Would you like to watch TV with my roommate and **me**?
3. My aunts are nice **women**.
4. My **mother's** brothers live in Venezuela.
5. Whose watch **is** this?
6. That blue car isn't **ours**.
7. The **teachers** are having a meeting next Monday.
8. Some students left **their** books in the classroom.
9. **Who's** finished with the test?
10. There are seven **people** in my family.

CHAPTER 7

Quiz 1, p. 90
2. noncount
3. count
4. noncount
5. noncount
6. noncount
7. count
8. noncount
9. count
10. noncount
11. noncount

Quiz 2, p. 90
2. money
3. sofas
4. fruit
5. songs
6. jewelry
7. weather
8. facts
9. mail
10. cars
11. words

Quiz 3, p. 91
1. homework
2. coffee
3. weather
4. clouds
5. tomatoes, meat
6. women
7. coins
8. money
9. fruit

Quiz 4, p. 91
2. a
3. an
4. an
5. a
6. an
7. a
8. an
9. a
10. an
11. a

Quiz 5, p. 92
1. an-singular count
some-plural count
some-noncount
2. some-noncount
some-plural count
an-singular count
3. some-noncount
some-plural count
a-singular count
a-singular count

Quiz 6, p. 92
1. an, some
2. some, an
3. an, some, a, some
4. a, some

Quiz 7, p. 93

A.
2. piece
3. bottle
4. tube
5. head
6. bunch

B.
2. pickles
3. water
4. candy/rice
5. rice/candy
6. soap

Quiz 8, p. 93

Possible answers:
1. a cup of
2. a piece of
3. a glass of
4. a piece of
5. a bowl of
6. a bowl of
7. a piece of
8. a piece of
9. a bowl of
10. a glass of

Quiz 9, p. 94

1. much
2. many
3. much
4. many
5. much
6. many
7. many
8. much
9. much
10. many

Quiz 10, p. 94

1. a little money
2. a few coins
3. a little cheese
4. a few apples
5. a little work
6. a few assignments
7. a few pictures
8. a little music
9. a few friends
10. a few cities

Quiz 11, p. 95

2. much
3. a
4. some, a few
5. many, a few
6. a little
7. a few, a jar of
8. a few
9. some, a little, much
10. an
11. some, a little

Quiz 12, p. 95

1. a, a, The, the
2. a, an, The, The
3. an, a, the, The, a
4. a, The, a, The, the, a

Quiz 13, p. 96

1. a, the, the
2. The, The, the
3. a, a
4. the
5. an

Quiz 14, p. 96

1. Ø
2. the
3. The
4. Ø
5. Ø
6. The
7. Ø
8. The
9. The
10. Ø

Quiz 15, p. 97

1. A: some, some/any
   B: any
2. A: some, any
   B: some
3. A: some
   B: some/any
4. A: some/any
   B: any

Quiz 16, p. 97

1. an
2. any
3. any
4. a
5. an
6. any
7. a
8. any
9. any
10. any

Quiz 17, p. 98

2. a
3. c
4. b
5. c
6. a
7. b
8. c
9. b
10. c
11. b
12. b
13. c
14. c
15. b
16. b

TEST 1, p. 99

A.
1. water
2. friends
3. assignments
4. work
5. help

B.
1. b
2. c
3. b
4. a
5. c
6. a
7. c
8. b
9. c
10. b

C.
1. a, an, The, the
2. the

D.
1. Ø
2. The
3. The
4. Ø

E.
1. Emily doesn't get **much/any mail**.
2. I need **some** advice./I need advice.
3. There's **an** orange for you in the refrigerator.
4. Do you want to listen to some **music** now?
5. How **many** chairs do you have in your room?
6. Kenji doesn't want **any** tea.

TEST 2, p. 101

A.
1. questions
2. jewelry
3. children
4. information
5. weather

B.
1. b
2. c
3. a
4. b
5. b
6. a
7. b
8. b
9. c
10. a

C.
1. the
2. the, The
3. a, an

D.
1. the
2. Ø
3. Ø
4. The

E.
1. Pablo doesn't want **any** cheese/Pablo doesn't **want cheese** on his hamburger.
2. We don't have **many/any** warm clothes.
3. …I want to look up some **words/a word**.
4. …He wants **a** glass of water.
5. A: Are you wearing **a** watch?…
6. I'd like **an** apple, please.

CHAPTER 8

Quiz 1, p. 103
1. was tired yesterday, too.
2. was busy yesterday, too.
3. were at school yesterday, too.
4. was on TV yesterday, too.
5. was in her office yesterday, too.
6. were in Chicago yesterday, too.
7. were at home yesterday, too.
8. was sick yesterday, too.
9. were on a trip yesterday, too.
10. was with my family yesterday, too.

Quiz 2, p. 104
1. wasn't
2. wasn't
3. weren't
4. wasn't
5. wasn't
6. weren't
7. wasn't
8. weren't
9. weren't
10. wasn't

Quiz 3, p. 105
1. A: Were Kazu and Keiko in Madrid last month
   B: they weren't
2. A: Was the weather in Seattle sunny yesterday
   B: it wasn't
3. A: Were you and Robin at a party last night
   B: we were
4. A: Was Mrs. Masson your teacher last year
   B: she was
5. A: Were you at the concert last weekend
   B: I wasn't

Quiz 4, p. 106
1. A: Was Martha on vacation last week
   B: she was
   A: was she
2. A: Were you at the library yesterday afternoon
   B: I wasn't
   A: were you
3. A: Were you and Edith late for class yesterday
   B: we were
   A: were you
4. A: Was Wesley in town last weekend
   B: he wasn't
   A: was he
5. A: Were the children at the zoo yesterday
   B: they weren't
   A: were they

Quiz 5, p. 107
1. A: Was Linda absent from class yesterday
   B: she was
2. A: Is Linda in class today
   B: she isn't
3. A: Are you nervous right now
   B: I'm not
4. A: Were you nervous on the first day of class
   B: I was
5. A: Was Olivia in Miami last summer
   B: Yes, she was
6. A: Is the weather in Miami usually hot in the summer
   B: it is
7. A: Were Omar and Zahra in town last week
   B: they weren't
8. A: Are Omar and Zahra out of town this week
   B: they aren't

Quiz 6, p. 108
1. was
2. was
3. was
4. was
5. was
6. were
7. were
8. was
9. were
10. were

Quiz 7, p. 108
2. watch, watched
3. plays, played
4. talk, talked
5. listened, listens
6. visited, visits

Quiz 8, p. 109

A.
1. last
2. last
3. yesterday
4. last
5. yesterday

B.
1. five minutes ago
2. seven months ago
3. three days ago
4. a (one) week ago
5. an (one) hour ago

Quiz 9, p. 110
1. saw
2. wrote
3. went
4. stood
5. put
6. got
7. ate
8. slept
9. did
10. came, sat

Quiz 10, p. 111
1. wrote, is writing
2. are, put
3. is raining, rained
4. get, got
5. saw, visits
6. ate, had, went, got, were

Quiz 11, p. 112
1. didn't come
2. didn't do
3. didn't play
4. weren't
5. didn't study
6. didn't go
7. didn't have
8. didn't call
9. didn't sit
10. wasn't

Quiz 12, p. 113

1. like
2. are
3. was
4. played
5. had
6. danced
7. enjoyed
8. was
9. like
10. didn't go
11 didn't have
12. am thinking
13. am
14. missed
15. am looking

Quiz 13, p. 114

1. A: Did Paul eat eggs for breakfast yesterday morning
   B: Yes, he did
2. A: Did Andrea go to a party yesterday evening
   B: No, she didn't
3. A: Did Wes and Travis camp by the lake last weekend
   B: Yes, they did
4. A: Did Ivan call Clara yesterday afternoon
   B: Yes, he did
5. A: Did you visit your grandparents two months ago
   B: Yes, we did
6. A: Did your sister write many texts yesterday
   B: Yes, she did
7. A: Did you see an interesting bird last week
   B: Yes, we did
8. A: Did Mr. Ross work in his office last Monday
   B: No, he didn't
9. A: Did you and George travel to Italy last summer
   B: Yes, we did
10. A: Did you sleep well last night
    B: No, I didn't

Quiz 14, p. 115

1. ran
2. bought
3. drove
4. taught
5. read
6. brought
7. rode
8. caught
9. drank
10. thought

Quiz 15, p. 116

2. rang
3. broke
4. took, flew
5. sang
6. paid
7. heard
8. sent
9. met
10. left

Quiz 16, p. 117

2. told
3. said
4. stole
5. began, lost
6. hung
7. found, wore
8. sold
9. tore

Quiz 17, p. 118

1. A: Did
   B: didn't, was, wasn't
2. A: Were
   B: weren't, were
3. A: Did
   B: did, were
4. A: were
   B: was
   A: Did
   B: did, was

Quiz 18, p. 119

1. wrote
2. was
3. helped
4. saw
5. studied
6. taught
7. left
8. told
9. rode
10. enjoyed
11. found
12. drove
13. got
14. finished
15. were

Quiz 19, p. 119

1. Mari **was** not in class yesterday.
2. Mrs. Douglas **taught** us a new song last week.
3. We didn't **come** to school last week. We were sick.
4. I **didn't** finish my homework yesterday evening. I **was** too tired.
5. Did Simone **go** to the concert **last** night?
6. Amanda is here now. She arrived **five minutes ago**.
7. Where **were** you yesterday?
8. **Did** Francisco **miss** the bus yesterday morning?

TEST 1, p. 120

A.
1. is, was
2. was, am
3. were, are

B.
1. took, asked
2. heard, told
3. visited, stayed

C.
1. isn't doing, rang, is talking
2. wasn't, didn't go
3. got, doesn't need
4. didn't walk, took, ride

D.
1. c, c
2. a, b
3. b, a
4. c, b

E.
1. Someone **stole** my camera a week ago.
2. Paula didn't **work** last Saturday.
3. **Last** night Olga and I studied grammar together.
4. Our teacher was sick yesterday. We **didn't** have class.
5. I got your email. It **came** yesterday.

TEST 2, p. 122

A.
1. am, was
2. were, are
3. is, were

B.
1. cooked, ate
2. met, talked
3. bought, paid

C.
1. wore, isn't wearing, doesn't like
2. didn't sleep, wants
3. takes, took
4. didn't play, wasn't, played

D.
1. c, b
2. a, c
3. a, b
4. a, c

E.
1. Patricia **brought** her friends to the picnic last Saturday.
2. Ali is here now. He came **five minutes ago.**
3. I didn't **see** Bruno at school last week. He was sick.
4. A lot of students **weren't** ready for the practice test yesterday.
5. Where **were you** last night? You didn't answer your phone.

CHAPTER 9

Quiz 1, p. 124

Answers may vary.

A.
2. was/did Sasha and Isabella have
3. did Sasha and Isabella invite
4. did the party start
5. did their friends go
6. did everyone stay

B.
1. you watch a movie last night
2. your sister study at the university last semester
3. you charge your phone yesterday
4. Jorge do his laundry last week
5. Marco and Luisa finish their homework yesterday

Quiz 2, p. 125
1. What did Tony and Anita eat for dinner?
2. Did Tony and Anita eat pizza for dinner?
3. Does Jin usually have noodles for lunch?
4. What does Jin usually have for lunch?
5. Did you get an iPad?
6. What did you get?
7. What does *decade* mean?
8. Does *muggy* mean "funny"?
9. What is Marissa doing?
10. Is Marissa talking on the phone?

Quiz 3, p. 126

A.
1. Who came to the party?
2. Who did Diana meet?
3. Who saved a lot of money?
4. Who did Helena come with?
5. Who are you studying with?
6. Who gave you a ride to school?

B.
1. a. a photo of Laurent, Maria
   b. Maria take a photo of, Laurent
2. a. Nina email, Ibrahim
   b. Ibrahim, Nina
3. a. the thief, the police
   b. the police catch, the thief
4. Ms. West teach, the students
   the students (English), Ms. West

Quiz 4, p. 127
1. When did Alex go to Greece?
2. What did Eduard wear to the meeting?
3. Where did the children go yesterday?
4. What time/When did the baby go to sleep?
5. Why did Monica stay up late?
6. Who asked a question?
7. What did you see at the museum?
8. Where did Frida eat lunch?
9. What time/When did Math class start?
10. Who did you see at the gym?

Quiz 5, p. 128
1. hurt, shut
2. forgot, lent, spent
3. hit, cost
4. gave, made, cut

Quiz 6, p. 128
1. won
2. drew
3. swam
4. blew, fell
5. knew, felt
6. grew
7. kept, threw

Quiz 7, p. 129
2. became
3. shook
4. built
5. hid
6. fed
7. held
8. bit
9. bent
10. fought

Quiz 8, p. 130
2. bought
3. carried
4. cost
5. drove
6. fell
7. fed
8. felt
9. forgot
10. grew
11. hid
12. lived
13. lost
14. needed
15. put
16. read
17. said
18. slept
19. smiled
20. stayed
21. taught
22. thought
23. tried
24. understood
25. wore
26. wrote

Quiz 9, p. 130

A.
1. 2, 1, b
2. 1, 2, a
3. 2, 1, a
4. 2, 1, b
5. 1, 2, b

B.
1. After he took the medicine, he felt better. OR
   He felt better after he took the medicine.
2. She lived in China before she came here. OR
   Before she came here, she lived in China.
3. After we ate dinner, we watched a movie on TV. OR
   We watched a movie on TV after we ate dinner.
4. I drank two glasses of water before I went jogging.
   OR
   Before I went jogging, I drank two glasses of water.
5. After they came home from school, they had a snack.
   OR
   They had a snack after they came home from school.

Quiz 10, p. 132

2. when her baby learned to walk. When her baby learned to walk, Faith clapped.
3. we saw tigers and zebras. We saw tigers and zebras when we went to the zoo.
4. she broke her arm. Ruth broke her arm when she fell on the ice.
5. when he went to the grocery store. When Kristos went to the grocery store, he bought some orange juice.
6. when it began to rain. When it began to rain, Mr. Wong opened his umbrella.

Quiz 11, p. 132

2. are doing, were doing
3. is reading, was reading
4. is raining, was raining
5. are sitting, were sitting
6. are talking, were talking

Quiz 12, p. 133

1. was cleaning, came
2. were playing, arrived
3. went, was raining
4. were watching, got
5. opened, was talking

Quiz 13, p. 134

1. While we were walking home yesterday afternoon, it started to snow.
   It started to snow while we were walking home yesterday afternoon.
2. Someone knocked on the door while I was taking a bath.
   While I was taking a bath, someone knocked on the door.
3. I fell asleep at my computer while I was trying to write an essay last night.
   While I was trying to write an essay last night, I fell asleep at my computer.
4. While Hyeri was practicing the piano, the lights suddenly went out.
   The lights suddenly went out while Hyeri was practicing the piano.
5. Joshua's calculator broke while he was studying math last night.
   While Joshua was studying math last night, his calculator broke.

Quiz 14, p. 134

1. called, was cooking, invited, had
2. forgot, was talking, rang, reached, turned, told

Quiz 15, p. 135

1. became, met
2. was, was swimming
3. won, moved
4. was studying
5. swam, gave
6. had

Quiz 16, p. 136

2. a	10. d
3. d	11. b
4. c	12. b
5. b	13. c
6. a	14. b
7. c	15. c
8. a	16. b
9. b	

Quiz 17, p. 137

1. begin, end, is, is driving, was driving
2. woke up, fed, feeds, gave, didn't like, didn't eat
3. was walking, dropped, blew, need

Quiz 18, p. 138

1. What **does** this word **mean**?
2. Yesterday I cleaned my room after I **came** home from school.
3. Why **didn't** you finish your homework last night?
4. I got a phone call while I was **washing** the dishes yesterday evening.
5. Where **did** Khaled **go** after class yesterday?
6. While Winston was playing baseball yesterday, he **fell** down on the grass and hurt his knee.
7. Who **did** you **dance** with at the party last night?
8. When we **played** basketball last Saturday, we didn't **win** the game.
9. Who **made** this cake? It's delicious.

TEST 1, p. 139

A.

1. threw	6. won
2. smiled	7. taught
3. built	8. held
4. enjoyed	9. added
5. cut	10. blew

B.
1. What did Alexander buy?
2. Why did you stay home yesterday?
3. Where did you study last night?
4. Who made the cake?
5. When did Shazia come home?
6. Who did you meet at the airport?

C.
1. were washing, came, helped, watched
2. put, was playing, fell, wanted, didn't have, spent, saw, felt
3. went, wanted, needed, tried, was waiting, found, bought, decided

D.
1. Tomas **lent** me ten dollars last week.
2. Who **did** you **see** at the library last night?
3. Did Victor **go** to the grocery store yesterday?
4. Maria **flew** to Puerto Rico a month ago.
5. Mustafa didn't **answer** his phone yesterday.
6. After she **went** to bed, the phone rang.
7. Hannah **lost** her purse on the subway.

TEST 2, p. 141

A.
1. knew	6. kept
2. asked	7. hit
3. became	8. dropped
4. planned	9. fought
5. forgot	10. thought

B.
1. Where did Song spend last weekend?
2. Why did Sam lend money to Nikki?
3. Who answered the phone?
4. When did Katrina leave home?
5. What was Pat building last weekend?
6. Who did Paula sit next to yesterday?

C.
1. arrived, was telling, missed, asked
2. was driving, turned, heard, got, found, bought, loaded, listened
3. had, went, were swimming, bit, didn't hurt, felt, didn't believe, told

D.
1. Why **didn't** Maria go to school yesterday?
2. Marco **grew** up in Brazil.
3. I **was talking** on the phone to Jenny last night when my parents came home.
4. What **does** *attic* **mean**?
5. Who **drew** that picture? It's beautiful.
6. Bruno **didn't finish** his assignments before class yesterday.
7. I burned my finger while I **was cooking** dinner last night.

CHAPTER 10

Quiz 1, p. 143
2. am going to walk to school/stay home tomorrow
3. is going to go to bed early tonight/stay home tomorrow
4. are going buy a new, faster one soon
5. is going to have a glass of water
6. are going to get up early/go to bed early tonight
7. are going to study together after school
8. is going to stay home tomorrow/go to bed early tonight
9. is going to take a lot of photos
10. am going to go shopping
11. is going to bake a cake

Quiz 2, p. 144
1. A: Is Julia going to work
   B: she isn't
2. is Paul going to see
3. are you going to live
4. A: Is Misun going to go
   B: she is
5. A: Are they going to bring
   B: they aren't
6. are you going to do
7. are we going to eat
8. A: Are Anna and Jose going to get
   B: they are
9. A: Is Jared going to visit
   B: he is
10. is Laura going to call

Quiz 3, p. 145

A.
1. John and Sue are taking the train to Los Angeles
2. Kate is leaving for Italy
3. May is driving to Miami
4. I am flying to Mazatlan
5. Bev is visiting her nephew in Chicago

B.
2. future
3. present
4. future
5. future
6. present

Quiz 4, p. 146
1. ago	9. next
2. in	10. last
3. last	11. tomorrow
4. Yesterday	12. Next
5. last	13. ago
6. tomorrow	14. tomorrow
7. in	15. In
8. yesterday	

Quiz 5, p. 147
Answers may vary.
1. a couple of days ago	6. a few years ago
2. in ten days	7. in a month
3. two hours ago	8. in a couple of months
4. in a few hours	9. in a week
5. twenty years ago	10. one week ago

Quiz 6, p. 148
1. is working	6. is going to do
2. is going to teach	7. is going to finish
3. went	8. worked
4. watched	9. is washing
5. are watching	10. visited

Quiz 7, p. 149

1. b, c
2. a
3. a, c
4. a, b, c
5. a, c
6. b, c
7. b, c
8. a, b
9. a, b, c
10. a, b

Quiz 8, p. 150

2. will make
3. will bring
4. will go
5. won't rain
6. won't need
7. will visit
8. will arrive
9. won't forget
10. won't be
11. will send

Quiz 9, p. 150

1. A: Will Eric be at the library this evening?
   B: he will
   A: Where will he be?
2. A: Will you cook dinner tonight?
   B: I will
   A: When will dinner be ready?
3. A: Will Rob and Tara be at the meeting tomorrow?
   B: they won't
   A: Where will they be?
   A: When will they come back?

Quiz 10, p. 151

1. A: Does Fatima call
   B: she does, don't see, talk, like
2. A: Did you go
   B: I didn't, played, started, waited, didn't stop, are going to finish/will finish
3. A: Are you using
   B: I am, am looking, am going to visit/will visit, am going to take/will take, am trying
   A: want
   B: am going to finish/will finish

Quiz 11, p. 152

1. aren't, Is a tomato
2. was, wasn't, were, Were you
3. aren't going to be/won't be, am going to be/will be, is going to be/will be, Are you and Jan going to be/Will you and Jan be

Quiz 12, p. 152

1. A: Do you exercise
   B: do, go
   A: Did you go
   B: didn't, was, went
   A: Are you going to be/Will you be
   B: won't, am going to be/will be
2. A: Did you talk
   B: didn't, tried, didn't answer, was she
   A: was, walked, saw, didn't know, left, called, came, asked
   B: Is Natasha
   A: is

Quiz 13, p. 153

1. I'm **not going** to go to the grocery store tomorrow.
2. Next weekend my grandmother **will make** a cake for my birthday.

3. **Did** you **go** to the concert last Saturday?
4. When **will you** see Ms. Reed?
5. My husband is going to meet me here in a few **minutes**.
6. I **will buy** a present for my sister tomorrow.
7. **Will Tom** come next week?
8. **Last** night/**Yesterday** I watched an interesting program on the Internet.
9. Where **is Sophia** going to live next year?
10. My friends didn't **arrive** on time yesterday.

TEST 1, p. 154

A.
A: am going to leave
B: are you going to come
A: is going to come, are going to study
B: Is Gina going to have
A: isn't

B.
A: (I)'ll see/will see
B: will you be
A: won't be/will not be
B: Will you do
A: will, (I)'ll clean/will clean

C.
1. next
2. ago
3. yesterday
4. tomorrow
5. in
6. last

D.
1. A: Is the post office
   A: did it close
   B: is going to open/will open
2. rang, didn't answer, didn't want, wanted
3. is, was, will be

E.
1. Chris **will call** me in a few minutes.
2. Where **will you** spend tomorrow night?
3. Jason **is** going to play computer games with his friends next Saturday.
4. **Will Anne/Is Anne going to** live in New York next year?
5. I'll see you in a couple of **days.**

TEST 2, p. 156

A.
A: are you going to do
B: is going to work/am going to take
A: are you going to go
B: are going to fly
A: are going to have

B.
A: Will Professor Stevens be
B: won't
A: will she be
B: will be
A: will come
B: will see

C.

1. in
2. tomorrow
3. next
4. ago
5. last
6. Yesterday

D.

1. is going to meet/will meet, talked
2. A: Are you going to see/Will you see
   B: aren't going to be/won't be, are going to be/will be
3. don't have, am going to write/will write, doesn't expect
4. A: Do bats have
   B: are not

E.

1. What time **are you** going to arrive tomorrow?
2. Maria will **take** an important test later this afternoon.
3. Diana's boss **won't come** to the meeting with her next Monday.
4. **Will you** be in town next month?
5. **I'm/I am** not going to go to work tomorrow.

CHAPTER 11

Quiz 1, p. 158

1. will call
2. will not/won't go
3. will play, may/might watch
4. may/might play, may/might rain, will check
5. will study, may/might become
6. may/might not see

Quiz 2, p. 159

A.

1. may be
2. may be
3. Maybe, may be
4. Maybe, may be

B.

1. Maybe Luisa is in the kitchen. Luisa may be in the kitchen.
2. Maybe I won't be home for dinner. I may not be home for dinner.

Quiz 3, p. 160

1. We may eat dinner at a restaurant tonight.
2. I might go to the science center next weekend.
3. Maybe it will be sunny tomorrow.
4. We might watch a movie on TV this evening.
5. Emily and Joshua may get married next fall.
6. Maybe I'll be in Paris in the spring.
7. I may do my laundry in a couple of days.
8. Charles might read something interesting online tonight.
9. Maybe you'll feel better tomorrow.
10. My parents may go to the opera on Saturday.

Quiz 4, p. 161

1. _1_ I type the email.
   _2_ I send the email.
   a. Before I send the email, I am going to type it. OR I am going to type the email before I send it.
   b. After I type the email, I am going to send it. OR I am going to send the email after I type it.
2. _2_ The students take the test.
   _1_ The students study hard.
   a. Before the students take the test, they are going to study hard. OR The students are going to study hard before they take the test.
   b. After the students study hard, they are going to take the test. OR The students are going to take the test after they study hard.
3. _1_ I read this book.
   _2_ I return the book to the library.
   a. After I read this book, I'm going to return it to the library. OR I'm going to return this book to the library after I read it.
   b. Before I return this book to the library, I'm going to read it. OR I'm going to read this book before I return it to the library.
4. _2_ I take a long trip by car.
   _1_ I buy gasoline.
   a. After I buy gasoline, I'm going to take a long trip by car. OR I'm going to take a long trip by car after I buy gasoline.
   b. Before I take a long trip by car, I am going to buy gasoline. OR I'm going to buy gasoline before I take a long trip by car.
5. _1_ The children build the kite.
   _2_ The children fly the kite.
   a. After the children build the kite, they are going to fly it. OR The children are going to fly the kite after they build it.
   b. Before the children fly the kite, they are going to build it. OR The children are going to build the kite before they fly it.

Quiz 5, p. 162

1. am going to call, leave
2. finishes, is going to listen
3. are going to buy, go
4. comes, am going to clean
5. is going to give, buys

Quiz 6, p. 162

1. are going to/will worry, come
2. am going to/will be, don't win
3. isn't, is not going to/won't wash
4. have, am not going to/won't go
5. is going to/will write, has

Quiz 7, p. 163

2. present habit
3. future activity
4. future activity
5. present habit
6. present habit
7. future activity
8. present habit
9. future activity
10. present habit
11. future activity

Quiz 8, p. 164

1. eats, always has
2. am going to/will visit, go
3. goes, is going to/will drink
4. often watch, go
5. is, usually go
6. gets, is going to/will buy
7. meets, usually get
8. often call, feel
9. talks, always listen
10. is going to/will send, lands

Quiz 9, p. 165

1. is Laura doing, is writing
2. does Alex do, sleeps
3. did you do, studied
4. are you going to do, are going to do
5. did Emilio do, downloaded

Quiz 10, p. 165

3. Jesse **might not/might** play soccer next Saturday.
4. correct
5. If **I have** a cold tomorrow, I won't come to class.
6. Toshiko **may/will come** to volleyball practice tomorrow.
7. What **is** your sister doing right now?
8. correct
9. When Yao plays basketball, everyone always **watches**.
10. What did they **do** last weekend?
11. If it snows tomorrow, we **will wear** warm clothes.
12. I will finish my homework after I **check** my email.

Quiz 11, p. 166

1. is going to/will be, read
2. do you usually eat, usually eat, have
3. happened, fell, Did you break, spent
4. lost, didn't lose, is
5. Are you going to/Will you be, am going to/will stay, help, is going to/will be
6. forgot, left, blew, am going to/will clean

Quiz 12, p. 166

2. d
3. b
4. a
5. a
6. c
7. b
8. d
9. b
10. c
11. c

TEST 1, p. 168

A.
1. It might be sunny tomorrow.
2. I might not be in class on Friday.
3. Don may send me a text later.
4. Maybe Monica will practice the piano after school.
5. We may not be at the meeting tonight.

B.
1. go, am going to buy
2. am going to call, leave
3. gets up, is going to make
4. aren't going to do, don't get
5. are, are going to stop

C.
1. visit, tells
2. are going to have, begin
3. am going to check, watch
4. has, shares
5. see, am going to lend

D.
1. _1_ I turn on my computer.
   _2_ I check my email.
   I am going to turn on my computer before I check my email. OR
   Before I check my email, I am going to turn on my computer.
2. _1_ Elly reads for 30 minutes.
   _2_ Elly goes to sleep.
   After Elly reads for 30 minutes, she is going to go to sleep. OR
   Elly is going to go to sleep after she reads for 30 minutes.

E.
1. are you going to do
2. did the kids do
3. does your dad do

F.
1. The children **may be** at the park now.
2. correct
3. correct
4. Rosa will cook dinner after **she goes** to the grocery store.
5. What **is** Pablo going to do next weekend?

TEST 2, p. 170

A.
1. The plane from Chicago may be late.
2. Maybe Jin won't buy a new car this year.
3. Travis might become a computer engineer.
4. I may not get home until late tonight.
5. Maybe Joe and Mia will have a baby soon.

B.
1. am going to change, go
2. is going to go, has
3. doesn't feel, am going to call
4. are going to take, come
5. graduates, is going to go

C.
1. reads, puts
2. cancel, isn't
3. get, am going to rest
4. are, listen
5. need, am going to ask

D.
1. _1_ Our teacher tells us the homework.
   _2_ Our teacher allows us to leave class.
   Before our teacher allows us to leave class, he/she is going to tell us the homework. OR
   Our teacher is going to tell us the homework before he/she allows us to leave class.

2. **2** I give some money to my brother.
   1 I get some money from the bank.
   After I get some money from the bank, I am going to give some money to my brother. OR
   I am going to give some money to my brother after I get some money from the bank.

E.
1. do your parents do
2. are you going to do
3. did Alexander do

F.
1. Julia **might move** to Miami next fall.
2. correct
3. If **we have** class on your next birthday, we'll bring a cake for you.
4. What do you **do** after you wake up every morning?
5. Rick is going to finish his homework before he **goes** to bed tonight.

CHAPTER 12

Quiz 1, p. 172
1. Fish can swim.
2. A newborn baby can't talk.
3. Dogs can't ride bicycles.
4. A rabbit can jump.
5. Humans can't fly.
6. A cow can't dance.
7. A monkey can climb a tree.
8. Cats can't read.
9. A bird can sing.
10. My teacher can speak English.

Quiz 2, p. 172
Listening Script
Answers are underlined.
1. Tim <u>can</u> ride a bicycle.
2. Anna <u>can't</u> write in Arabic.
3. Mehmet <u>can</u> sew a button on a shirt.
4. Chris <u>can</u> cook Chinese food.
5. Ivan <u>can't</u> eat with chopsticks.
6. Sophia <u>can</u> play the violin.
7. David <u>can't</u> drive a stick-shift car.
8. Laura <u>can</u> whistle.
9. John <u>can't</u> fly a plane.
10. Vlado <u>can't</u> touch the ceiling.

Quiz 3, p. 173
A.
1. A: Can Kimmy water ski?
   B: Yes, she can.
2. A: Can you come to the meeting?
   B: No, I can't.
3. A: Can Max ride a motorcycle?
   B: No, he can't.
4. A: Can you make French toast?
   B: Yes, I can.
5. A: Can Lisa and Roger dance the tango?
   B: Yes, they can.

B.
1. Where can I buy
2. When can you fix
3. When can Ms. Lee meet
4. Where can I get
5. When can the boys help

Quiz 4, p. 174
1. A: Do you know how to play
   B: know how to play
2. A: Does Mia know how to make
   B: doesn't know how to make
3. A: Do cats know how to catch
   B: know how to catch
4. A: Do you know how to fix
   B: don't know how to fix
5. A: Does Tony know how to grow
   B: knows how to grow

Quiz 5, p. 175
1. can
2. couldn't
3. can't
4. can't
5. couldn't
6. can
7. could, can't
8. could, can

Quiz 6, p. 175
1. Paloma learned to play the guitar last year. Now she can **play** it very well.
2. When I was five years old, I **could** ride my bike with no hands.
3. We don't have any matches. We **can't light** the candles.
4. Could your **parents speak** English before they came to this country?
5. Adam is busy after school today. He **can't** go to the club meeting.
6. Where **can we** find a vegetarian restaurant?
7. Freddy **can't** wiggle his ears.
8. Could **you write** your name when you were four years old?
9. I couldn't **wash** my clothes last night because I didn't have any laundry soap.
10. David **can't** speak Spanish.

Quiz 7, p. 176
1. I will be able to meet you at the library at 3:30 tomorrow.
2. Toshi and Mika weren't able to go to the US to study English.
3. Dogs aren't able to talk.
4. My daughter was able to read before the age of five.
5. I am not able to touch my ear with my elbow.
6. Is Anya able to speak more than two languages?
7. My father won't be able to come to the meeting next Monday.
8. Were you able to hear the difference between those two sounds?
9. You are able to cook better than me.
10. I wasn't able to find my keys this morning.

Quiz 8, p. 177

1. too
2. very
3. too
4. very
5. very
6. too
7. too
8. too
9. very
10. too

Quiz 9, p. 178

3. I **wasn't** able to stay at school for the meeting yesterday.
4. I **will help** you tomorrow afternoon. OR I **can help** you tomorrow afternoon.
5. I **couldn't finish** my assignment last night. It was too long.
6. I went to Hawaii last January. I **was able to/could** go to the beach every day when I was there.
7. correct
8. Ali is very strong. He **can lift** his desk with one hand.
9. This curry rice is **too** spicy. I can't eat it.
10. correct
11. Alec **knows** how to speak English very well.
12. I **ate** a lot of noodles for dinner last night.

TEST 1, p. 179

A.
1. can fly
2. can't read
3. can't hear
4. can buy
5. can't drive

B.
1. Can you speak, can't
2. Can Maggie ride, can
3. can I find

C.
1. couldn't
2. can't
3. can't
4. couldn't
5. couldn't

D.
1. Eduardo knows how to speak two languages.
2. I wasn't able to sleep last night.
3. Ms. Lin will be able to call you back tomorrow.
4. Gina doesn't know how to wiggle her eyebrows.
5. Were you able to understand the lecture?

E.
1. very
2. too
3. too
4. very
5. too

F.
1. I **wasn't** able to swim when I was three years old.
2. Billy **knows** how to ride a bike.
3. Sometimes I **can't** understand the teacher.
4. We couldn't **watch** the movie last night.
5. Some fish can swim **very** fast.

TEST 2, p. 181

A.
1. can't see
2. can help
3. can't pay
4. can teach
5. can lift

B.
1. Can you spell, can
2. can Jane get
3. Can Tomas wiggle, can't

C.
1. couldn't
2. can't
3. can't
4. couldn't
5. can't

D.
1. My grandfather was able to play the guitar very well.
2. Fish aren't able to live on land.
3. Do you know how to write a compound sentence?
4. We weren't able to find fresh flowers at the supermarket.
5. My daughter knows how to eat with chopsticks.

E.
1. too
2. very
3. too
4. too
5. very

F.
1. When I was younger, I **could** stand on my head.
2. The music is **too** loud. I can't hear what you are saying.
3. Mrs. Park grew up in Korea, so she can **speak** Korean.
4. **Does** your brother know how to fix a car?
5. Dave **can come** to the picnic next weekend. OR Dave **will be able to come** to the picnic next weekend.

CHAPTER 13

Quiz 1, p. 183

A.
2. should call the police
3. should put on a warm sweater
4. should drive more carefully
5. should wash it

B.
1. shouldn't
2. should
3. shouldn't
4. should
5. shouldn't
6. should

Quiz 2, p. 184

1. have to go
2. do you have to get up, don't have to get up
3. Did he have to work, didn't have to work
4. have to show, don't have to pay
5. had to drive, did they have to go, had to pick up

Quiz 3, p. 185

A.
2. must not
3. must
4. must not
5. must
6. must

B.
1. must not
2. doesn't have to
3. must not
4. don't have to
5. must not

Quiz 4, p. 186

2. a
3. c
4. a
5. b
6. a

7. b
8. b
9. c
10. b
11. c

Quiz 5, p. 187

Answers will vary.
1. Mohammed: May I please come in?
   Prof. Costa: Yes, of course.
2. Jan: Could I please have a cup of hot tea?
   Waiter: Certainly.
   Jan: Thank you.
3. Carrie: Can I see your tablet computer?
   Alexis: Sure.
4. Suzanne: Could I please look at your calendar for a minute?
   Anna: Of course. Here it is.
   Suzanne: Thanks.

Quiz 6, p. 188

Answers will vary.
1. Karen: Could you please hold my books for a minute?
   Jeff: I'd be glad to.
   Karen: Thanks.
2. Kenji: Could you turn down your music?
   Hiro: No problem.
3. Prof. Koh: Would you please turn on the light?
   Fatima: Yes, of course.
   Prof. Koh: Thank you.
4. Ms. Martin: Would you take this package to the post office?
   Linda: Certainly.

Quiz 7, p. 189

A.
2. D
3. A
4. C
5. B
6. F

B.
Answers will vary.
2. Drink some hot tea.
3. Take some medicine/aspirin.
4. Lie down.
5. Sleep.
6. Go to the doctor.

Quiz 8, p. 190

1. to
2. Ø
3. Ø
4. to
5. Ø

6. Ø
7. to
8. Ø
9. to
10. Ø

Quiz 9, p. 191

2. b
3. b
4. a
5. c
6. a

7. a
8. b
9. c
10. b
11. c

Quiz 10, p. 192

1. b
2. b
3. a
4. b
5. c

6. c
7. a
8. c
9. b
10. a

Quiz 11, p. 194

A.
2. Let's watch a comedy.
3. Let's hurry.
4. Let's leave by 5:30 at the latest.
5. Let's turn on some music.
6. Let's go to the supermarket.

B.
Answers will vary.
2. Let's have a party.
3. Let's go to the museum.
4. Let's go shopping.
5. Let's buy a new one.
6. Let's stay home.

Quiz 12, p. 195

1. If Kim wants to be healthy, he should **exercise** three times a week.
2. I forgot my dictionary at home. **Could/Would** you please lend me yours?
3. I **had to go** to the dentist yesterday.
4. The stove is hot. **Don't** touch it!
5. My father has to **pay** a lot of taxes every year.
6. Would you please **pass** the hot sauce?
7. Let's **go** for a walk after dinner.
8. Did you **have** to go to school yesterday?
9. It's time for the concert to start. Please **be** quiet.
10. You **must have** a passport to travel to foreign countries.

TEST 1, p. 196

A.
1. should study
2. shouldn't eat
3. shouldn't drive
4. should stay
5. should wait

B.
1. has to leave, does he have to be, has to be
2. had to go, did she have to go
3. Do I have to eat

C.
1. don't have to
2. must not
3. doesn't have to
4. don't have to
5. must not

D.

1. c	6. c
2. a	7. b
3. a	8. a
4. b	9. c
5. b	10. b

E.
1. Where **do** you have to go now?
2. Will you **be able to** bake a cake for Jin's birthday? OR
   Can you bake a cake for Jin's birthday?
3. If Wang wants to improve his English, he should **listen** to English on the radio and the TV.
4. **Turn** off the light please. Thanks.
5. Did Jose **have** to study last night?

TEST 2, p. 198

A.
1. shouldn't watch
2. shouldn't spend
3. should brush
4. should ask
5. shouldn't carry

B.
1. had to work, Does she have to work
2. don't have to make, have to stay
3. do we have to do

C.
1. don't have to
2. must not
3. doesn't have to
4. must not
5. must not

D.

1. c	6. b
2. a	7. c
3. a	8. c
4. c	9. a
5. c	10. a

E.
1. Christos can't **go** to the soccer game with us tomorrow.
2. I **had to go** to the post office yesterday.
3. Please **stop** talking. I can't hear the movie.
4. **Do** you have to go to work tomorrow?
5. We **will be able to** bring food to the picnic next Saturday. OR
   We **can** bring food to the picnic next Saturday.

CHAPTER 14

Quiz 1, p. 200

A.
1. Her mother always wears <u>red</u> lipstick.
2. I drank a cup of <u>hot</u> tea.
3. Katya lives in the <u>big</u> house across the street.
4. My husband is an <u>honest</u> businessman.
5. You should wear <u>comfortable</u> shoes to work.

B.
1. I got a pair of <u>garden</u> gloves at J&J Hardware.
2. He always listens to that <u>radio</u> program on Saturdays.
3. Cathleen washed her <u>coffee</u> cup.
4. The <u>hotel</u> room had a window overlooking the park.
5. Alice gets many <u>text</u> messages every day.

Quiz 2, p. 201

A.
1. history book
2. toy store
3. concert tickets
4. house plants
5. office building

B.
1. small vegetable market
2. fresh fruit salad
3. long train trip
4. difficult math problem
5. favorite movie star

Quiz 3, p. 202

1. white plastic	6. big brown
2. short blond	7. funny British
3. dirty little	8. popular new Italian
4. important European	9. thick leather
5. soft cotton	10. big old American

Quiz 4, p. 203

3. Yolanda is a **young intelligent/an intelligent young** woman.
4. My cousin has **beautiful big blue** eyes.
5. correct
6. Josh bought **an expensive diamond** ring for Emily.
7. A **polite middle-aged** man carried my heavy suitcases upstairs for me.
8. My friends gave me a **delicious birthday** cake.
9. A **yellow school** bus stops in front of my house every morning.
10. correct
11. **A friendly American** student welcomed the new international students to campus.
12. Soccer is **a popular outdoor** sport in many countries.

Quiz 5, p. 204
Answers will vary.

2. feel nervous	7. feel sick
3. look comfortable	8. smell wonderful
4. feel proud	9. look dirty
5. tastes sour	10. tastes delicious
6. sounds exciting	11. sounds confusing

Quiz 6, p. 205

2. quickly
3. well
4. good
5. busy
6. neatly
7. fast
8. fast
9. fluently
10. slowly
11. quiet

Quiz 7, p. 205

1. Some of
2. Almost all of/Most of
3. All of
4. Most of
5. Some of
6. All of
7. Most of
8. Almost all of/Most of
9. Most of
10. All of

Quiz 8, p. 206

1. is
2. is
3. are
4. carry
5. was
6. have
7. were
8. was
9. were
10. wear

Quiz 9, p. 206

1. Does
2. likes
3. waiter, is
4. people, want
5. tastes
6. student, has
7. Does
8. Do, students
9. is
10. Is

Quiz 10, p. 207

1. something
2. Someone/Somebody
3. anyone/anybody/someone/somebody
4. anything, something
5. something
6. someone/somebody
7. anything, anyone/anybody, anything

Quiz 11, p. 208

1. a, b
2. a
3. a, b
4. b
5. b

Quiz 12, p. 209

1. Our teacher usually opens every **window** in the class-room.
2. Would you like a bowl of delicious **vegetable** soup?
3. Sami didn't eat **anything** for lunch.
4. Flora plays the violin very **well**.
5. I bought a beautiful **red leather** bag yesterday.

6. Most of the **apples are** rotten. OR Most of the **apple is** rotten.
7. Our teacher always talks **loudly**.
8. Matt knew **something** about the homework assignment.
9. Half of the students in the class **speak** Arabic well.
10. We had an **easy** grammar test last week.

Quiz 13, p. 210

2. b
3. c
4. a
5. d
6. b
7. c
8. b
9. c
10. d
11. c

TEST 1, p. 211

A.
1. beautiful Italian shoes
2. an interesting modern building
3. an old French recipe
4. small, blue, plastic purse

B.
1. hard
2. carefully
3. happy
4. quiet, quietly
5. well

C.
1. Do, people
2. is
3. enjoys
4. are
5. game, was
6. people, live
7. room, is
8. are

D.
1. b
2. a
3. b
4. a
5. a and b
6. a
7. b
8. a

E.
1. I forgot my lunch. Now I don't have **anything** to eat!
2. This chocolate cake tastes **sweet**.
3. Susan drives an old black car to work every **day**.
4. I need to put these flowers in some water. Does anyone have a **flower** vase?
5. Some of the people in this room **are** wearing blue jeans.

TEST 2, p. 213

A.
1. thick wool sweater
2. tiny Korean restaurant
3. a beautiful old ring
4. heavy, brown, paper bags

B.
1. fast
2. clear
3. late
4. loud, loudly
5. good

C.
1. is
2. student, has
3. was
4. Does, teacher
5. rooms, are
6. vases, are
7. smells
8. speaks

D.
1. b
2. b
3. a and b
4. a
5. a
6. b
7. b
8. b

E.
1. Does anybody want a bowl of hot **vegetable** soup for lunch?
2. Some of the animals in the zoo **are** from Africa.
3. My classmate feels **sad** today.
4. I need a big bag. I can't carry **anything** in this little backpack.
5. **Most/Almost all** of my friends live in Brazil.

CHAPTER 15

Quiz 1, p. 215
1. taller than
2. more interesting than
3. busier than
4. better than
5. cheaper than
6. farther/further . . . than
7. noisier than
8. more important than
9. worse . . . than
10. friendlier than

Quiz 2, p. 216
2. shorter than, the shortest
3. funnier than, the funniest
4. worse than, the worst
5. more difficult than, the most difficult
6. happier than, the happiest
7. bigger than, the biggest
8. more nervous than, the most nervous
9. farther/further than, the farthest/furthest
10. wetter than, the wettest
11. more boring than, the most boring

Quiz 3, p. 216
1. the fastest
2. the most delicious
3. the curliest
4. the hottest
5. the worst
6. the most beautiful
7. the deepest
8. the highest
9. the most popular
10. the most important

Quiz 4, p. 217
1. the biggest
2. the deepest
3. larger than
4. the busiest
5. The smallest
6. the most beautiful
7. the most popular
8. older than
9. more interesting than
10. the scariest

Quiz 5, p. 218

A.
1. one of the largest cities
2. one of the most beautiful bridges
3. one of the busiest airports
4. one of the best places
5. one of the most serious problems

B.
Answers will vary.
1. *The Guilt Trip* is **one of the funniest movies** of 2013.
2. Chinese is **one of the most difficult languages** in the world.
3. Chuck is **one of the shortest people** in our class.
4. Anne Hathaway is **one of the most famous movie stars** in the world.
5. Yellowstone Park is **one of the most interesting places** in the USA.

Quiz 6, p. 219
1. more quietly than
2. the most carefully
3. later than
4. the earliest
5. better than
6. harder than
7. more clearly than
8. the best
9. the most quickly
10. more fluently than

Quiz 7, p. 220
1. better than
2. the quietest
3. more slowly than
4. the fastest
5. the most fluently
6. easier than
7. the funniest
8. harder than
9. the worst
10. the most interesting
11. softer than
12. more carefully than
13. the most loudly
14. the slowest
15. more beautiful than

Quiz 8, p. 221

A.
2. is similar to
3. are the same
4. are different
5. is the same as
6. are similar/are different

B.
1. Hans and Paulo's apartments are **the** same size.
2. Bats and birds are **different**.
3. A college is similar **to** a university.
4. My English teacher is very different **from** my Math teacher.
5. My sister's eyes are the same color **as** my eyes.

Quiz 9, p. 222
1. like
2. alike
3. like, alike
4. like
5. like
6. like
7. alike
8. alike
9. like

Quiz 10, p. 222

2. sick
3. hardworking
4. thirsty
5. cheap
6. early
7. young
8. serious
9. boring
10. married

Quiz 11, p. 223

1. wasn't
2. does
3. didn't
4. can
5. aren't
6. were
7. don't
8. will
9. isn't
10. did

Quiz 12, p. 224

2. c
3. c
4. a
5. d
6. b
7. c
8. c
9. d
10. a
11. b

Quiz 13, p. 225

1. Eduardo's backpack is the same **as** mine.
2. Tran works hard, but his roommate **doesn't.** Tran's roommate is **lazier.**
3. A fly is different **from** a bee in many ways.
4. Health is more important **than** money.
5. The weather is **colder** this week than last week.
6. In my opinion, the Bluebird Restaurant is **the** worst restaurant in this city.
7. Professor Kondo's tests are **more difficult** than Professor Lee's tests.
8. Helena sings more **beautifully** than Gina.
9. Tennis balls and golf balls aren't **the** same size. Tennis balls are **larger** than golf balls.
10. The Yangtze River is one of **the** longest **rivers** in the world.
11. This art history book is **more interesting** than that psychology book.
12. Tracy's earrings are similar **to** yours. In other words, her earrings are **like** yours.

TEST 1, p. 226

A.
1. older than
2. the prettiest
3. better than
4. more interesting than
5. the most important

B.
1. more quickly than
2. the most clearly
3. faster than
4. earlier than, the earliest

C.
1. stronger than, more easily than
2. the best students, the quietest student
3. the best

D.
1. aren't
2. will
3. don't
4. was
5. do

E.
Answers may vary.
1. A is the same as D.
2. B is similar to C.
3. A and D are alike.
4. E is different from F.
5. A is like D.
6. D and E are different.
7. A and D are the same.
8. B and C are similar.

F.
1. A library is different **from** a bookstore.
2. The weather in January is **colder** than the weather in December.
3. A pond is smaller **than** a lake.
4. Greenland is the **largest** island in the world.
5. The food at the school cafeteria is **worse** than the food at the airport cafeteria.
6. Spanish is **like** Portuguese in some ways.
7. An American football and a soccer ball aren't **the** same shape.

TEST 2, p. 228

A.
1. the most famous
2. easier than
3. more expensive than
4. wetter than, the wettest

B.
1. more slowly than, the most slowly
2. later than
3. the most fluently
4. better than

C.
1. more colorful than
2. the most beautifully
3. more intelligent, the best guitarists
4. funnier than

D.
1. doesn't
2. didn't
3. are
4. can
5. won't

E.
Answers may vary.
1. A and C are different.
2. D is similar to F.
3. A is like E.
4. C is the same as D.
5. A and B are similar.
6. D is different from E.
7. C and D are alike.
8. A and E are the same.

F.
1. My sister and I have **the** same last name.
2. Canada is larger **than** China in area.
3. I can see **better** with my contact lenses than with my glasses.
4. My son is the **tallest** child in his class.
5. Men's basketball and women's basketball are **alike** in many ways.
6. Yasuko's dictionary is different **from** mine.
7. My other book is **more interesting** than this one.

MIDTERM EXAM 1

1.	b	26.	d
2.	c	27.	d
3.	a	28.	a
4.	c	29.	d
5.	b	30.	b
6.	d	31.	c
7.	b	32.	c
8.	b	33.	b
9.	c	34.	a
10.	b	35.	b
11.	c	36.	d
12.	a	37.	c
13.	b	38.	a
14.	c	39.	d
15.	b	40.	b
16.	d	41.	c
17.	b	42.	a
18.	c	43.	b
19.	d	44.	d
20.	a	45.	c
21.	c	46.	a
22.	a	47.	b
23.	c	48.	b
24.	c	49.	d
25.	a	50.	c

MIDTERM EXAM 2

A.
1. often has, studies, is taking
2. usually have, tastes, don't eat
3. are thinking, wants, thinks
4. is, is shining, isn't
5. is wearing, look, hurt

B.
1. A: Does Wendy teach music?
   B: Yes, she does.
2. A: Are you watching a movie now?
   B: No, I'm not.
3. A: Do the girls play soccer every Saturday?
   B: Yes, they do.
4. A: Are the workers at Country Market usually helpful?
   B: Yes, they are.
5. A: Is Paulo studying at the library?
   B: Yes, he is.

C.
1. Where does Marta live?
2. What are you making?
3. How many students are there in your French class?
4. Why is Cecilia learning to dance?
5. How's the weather today?/What is the weather like today?

D.
1. an, on
2. at, from
3. There is, many
4. my, He
5. a, Some

E.
1. many tomatoes
2. much coffee
3. much homework
4. many friends
5. Many children

F.
1. I have **some** information about the driving test.
2. My mother needs to get a **bottle** of olive oil at the store.
3. **Whose** book is this?
4. I don't have **any** paper. Can I borrow some?
5. There's too much **traffic** in the city.
6. Our teacher gave us a **few** problems to do for homework.
7. My dad is eating breakfast in **the** kitchen.
8. **Your** coffee has sugar in it.
9. Joao has problems with his **teeth**. He has to go to the dentist.
10. **Pat's** car keys are in his coat pocket.

FINAL EXAM 1

1.	c	26.	d
2.	d	27.	c
3.	c	28.	b
4.	a	29.	b
5.	c	30.	d
6.	b	31.	d
7.	d	32.	a
8.	b	33.	c
9.	a	34.	c
10.	d	35.	c
11.	b	36.	b
12.	c	37.	a
13.	c	38.	c
14.	d	39.	d
15.	a	40.	d
16.	b	41.	c
17.	a	42.	a
18.	c	43.	d
19.	b	44.	a
20.	a	45.	c
21.	c	46.	b
22.	a	47.	c
23.	c	48.	d
24.	a	49.	b
25.	d	50.	c

FINAL EXAM 2

A.
1. is, enjoy
2. grew, started
3. became
4. got
5. won
6. is going to/will star, am going to watch/will watch
7. like

B.
1. am taking, feel
2. went, were traveling, met
3. sent, was driving
4. gets, uses, is checking

C.
1. A: Are Maiko and Anton sitting in the front row?
   B: Yes, they are.
2. A: Did you go to the supermarket last Saturday?
   B: No, I didn't.
3. A: Will Fatima make fish and rice for dinner?
   B: Yes, she will.

4. A: Does your car use much gas?
   B: No, it doesn't.
5. A: Was Jim planning to go to the party?
   B: Yes, he was.

D.
1. What was the program about?
2. When are Pat and Andrea going to go to Yellowstone Park?
3. What did you do last night?
4. Where is my tennis racket?
5. Why did Kevin go to the bank?

E.
1. any, my
2. ours
3. books, books'
4. a
5. an, the
6. Willy's, a little
7. vegetable
8. quickly
9. uses, Ø
10. anything

F.
1. Our basketball team **may/might** win the game tomorrow.
2. Can Trent **speak** Spanish well?
3. The movie was **very** funny. I enjoyed it.
4. Children **should** get 8-10 hours of sleep every night. It's healthy.
5. Clara **has** to take her driver's test next Friday.
6. Mr. Paxton **doesn't have to** work any more. He is retired.
7. **Please finish** your homework before you go out.
8. Fred is **more handsome** than his friend.
9. My dog is the **cutest** dog in the world.
10. Max and Mark are classmates. They have **the** same teacher.